FOREIGN FIELD RESEARCH PROGRAM
SPONSORED BY THE
OFFICE OF NAVAL RESEARCH
REPORT NO. 30

JAPANESE COLONIZATION IN EASTERN PARAGUAY

NORMAN R. STEWART

PUBLICATION 1490
NATIONAL ACADEMY OF SCIENCES
NATIONAL RESEARCH COUNCIL
WASHINGTON, D. C.   1967

Dedication

To the pioneers of La Colmena,
whose constant struggle against
enormous odds to fashion a better life has not tempered their
capacity for kindness, hospitality, and friendship.

Published Reports
of the
FOREIGN FIELD
RESEARCH
PROGRAM

The Foreign Field Research Program Reports are sponsored by the Division of Earth Sciences of the National Academy of Sciences - National Research Council, with the financial support of the Geography Branch, Office of Naval Research. Text editions of NAS-NRC out-of-print reports may be requested from University Microfilms, 300 N. Zeeb Road, Ann Arbor, Mich. 48106, which maintains a reprint program for this series. All other reports must be ordered from the publishers named.

REPORT NO.

1   V. H. Malmström, A Regional Geography of Iceland, NAS-NRC Publ. 584 (1958), 255 pp. (out of print).

2   A. F. Burghardt, The Political Geography of Burgenland, NAS-NRC Publ. 587 (1958), 352 pp. (out of print).

3   C. L. Dozier, Indigenous Tropical Agriculture in Central America, NAS-NRC Publ. 594 (1958), 134 pp. (out of print).

4   K. E. Webb, Geography of Food Supply in Central Minas Gerais, NAS-NRC Publ. 642 (1959), 110 pp. (out of print).

5   A. A. Michel, The Kabul, Kunduz, and Helmand Valleys and the National Economy of Afghanistan, NAS-NRC Publ. (1959), 441 pp. (out of print).

6   H. L. Slutsky, An Ecological Study of Total Mortality Among Guatemalan Preschool Children With Special Emphasis on Protein Malnutrition and Kwashiokor, NAS-NRC Publ. (1960), 194 pp. (out of print).

7   J. H. Butler, Manufacturing in the Concepción Region of Chile, NAS-NRC Publ. (1960), 106 pp. (out of print).

8 R. E. Nunley, The Distribution of Population in Costa Rica, NAS-NRC Publ. 743 (1960), 71 pp. (out of print).

9 R. F. Logan, The Central Namib Desert, South West Africa, NAS-NRC Publ. 758 (1960), 162 pp. (out of print).

10 *L. Tow, The Manufacturing Economy of Southern Rhodesia, NAS-NRC Publ. 850 (1960), 141 pp., $2.00.

11 R. E. Chardon, Geographic Aspects of Plantation Agriculture in Yucatan, NAS-NRC Publ. 876 (1961), 200 pp. (out of print).

12 *D. R. Hoy, Agricultural Land Use of Guadeloupe, NAS-NRC Publ. 884 (1961), 90 pp., $2.00.

13 *R. A. Helin, Economic Geographic Reorientation in Western Finnish Karelia: A Result of the Finno-Soviet Boundary Demarcations of 1940 and 1944, NAS-NRC Publ. 909 (1961), 124 pp., $2.00.

14 A. R. Pred, The External Relations of Cities During 'Industrial Revolution', Res. Pap. 76, Univ. of Chicago Press (1962), 113 pp., $4.00 (order from Univ. of Chicago, Dept. of Geography, Chicago, Ill. 60637).

15 J. F. Kolars, Tradition, Season, and Change in a Turkish Village, Res. Pap. 82, Univ. of Chicago Press (1963), 230 pp., $4.00 (order from Univ. of Chicago, Dept. of Geography, Chicago, Ill. 60637).

16 P. P. Vouras, The Changing Economy of Northern Greece Since World War II, Inst. for Balkan Studies, Thessaloniki (1962), 227 pp., $5.00 (order from Institute for Balkan Studies, Thessaloniki, Greece).

17 W. Blake, Jr., Geomorphology and Glacial Geology in Nordaustlandet, Spitsbergen, Geogr. Ann., Stockholm (in press; order from Geografiski Annaler, Stockholm, Sweden).

18 *A. W. Urquhart, Patterns of Settlement and Subsistence in Southwestern Angola, NAS-NRC Publ. 1096 (1963), 149 pp., $4.00.

19 *C. M. Hoskin, Recent Carbonate Sedimentation on Alacran Reef, Yucatan, NAS-NRC Publ. 1089 (1963), 160 pp., $2.50.

20 N. M. Shaffer, The Competitive Position of the Port of Durban, Studies in Geogr. 8, Northwestern Univ. Press (1965), 261 pp., $3.75 (order from Northwestern Univ. Press, Dept. of Geography, 1735 Benson Ave., Evanston, Ill. 60201).

21 C. R. Edwards, Aboriginal Watercraft on the Pacific Coast of South America, Ibero-Americana: 47, Univ. of Calif. Press (1965), 160 pp., $3.50 (order from Univ. of Calif. Press, 2223 Fulton St., Berkeley, Calif. 94704).

*Available from NAS-NRC. See list on back page of this folder.

22A L. M. and M. A. Talbot, The Wildebeest in Western Masailand, East Africa, Wildlife Monogr. 12, Wildlife Soc., Washington, D.C. (September, 1963), 88 pp., $1.00 (order from Wildlife Soc., 3900 Wisconsin Ave., N.W., Washington, D.C. 20016).

23 T. K. Chamberlain, Submarine Canyons and Sagami Trough, East Central Honshu, Japan, Geol. Soc. Amer. Bull., Vol. 75 (November, 1964), pp. 1117-1130 (order from Geol. Soc. of Amer., 231 East 46th St., New York, N.Y. 10017).

24 W. M. Denevan, The Aboriginal Cultural Geography of the Llanos de Mojos of Bolivia, Ibero-Americana: 48, Univ. of Calif. Press (1966), 185 pp., $4.00 (order from Univ. of Calif. Press, 2223 Fulton St., Berkeley, Calif. 94704).

25 *G. N. Nasse, Italo-Albanian Villages of Southern Italy, NAS-NRC Publ. 1149 (1964), 81 pp., $3.00.

26 A. D. Hill, The Changing Landscape of a Mexican Municipio, Villa Las Rosas, Chiapas, Res. Pap. 91, Univ. of Chicago Press (1964), 121 pp., $4.00 (order from Univ. of Chicago, Dept. of Geography, Chicago, Ill. 60637).

27 H. G. Barnum, Market Centers and Hinterlands in Baden-Württemberg, Res. Pap. 103, Univ. of Chicago Press (1966), 173 pp., $4.00 (order from Univ. of Chicago, Dept. of Geography, Chicago, Ill. 60637).

28 P. W. English, City and Village in Iran, Univ. of Wisconsin Press (1966), 204 pp., $6.75 (order from Univ. of Wisconsin Press, Madison, Wis. 53701).

29 L. R. Pederson, The Mining Industry of Norte Chico, Chile, Studies in Geogr. 11, Northwestern Univ. Press (1966), 305 pp., $3.75 (order from Northwestern Univ. Press, Evanston, Ill. 60201).

30 *N. R. Stewart, Japanese Colonization in Eastern Paraguay, NAS-NRC Publ. 1490 (1967), 202 pp., $7.75.

*Available from NAS-NRC. See list on back page of this folder.

ORDER FORM

FOREIGN FIELD
RESEARCH PROGRAM REPORTS

Publications listed below may be ordered on this form. Circle those wanted, indicate the number of copies of each book, and figure the total costs. Payment must accompany an order totaling $3.00 or less. Please return the form to Printing and Publishing Office, National Academy of Sciences - National Research Council, 2101 Constitution Ave., Washington, D.C. 20418.

PUBLICATION NO.	PRICE	COPIES ORDERED
850 (Report 10)	$2.00	_____
884 (Report 12)	$2.00	_____
909 (Report 13)	$2.00	_____
1089 (Report 19)	$2.50	_____
1096 (Report 18)	$4.00	_____
1149 (Report 25)	$3.00	_____
1490 (Report 30)	$7.75	_____

PRINTING AND PUBLISHING OFFICE
NATIONAL ACADEMY OF SCIENCES
2101 CONSTITUTION AVE.
WASHINGTON, D.C. 20418

☐ I enclose $_____. Please send the books circled. (Payment must accompany an order totaling $3.00 or less.)

☐ Please supply invoice.

Please ship publications checked above to:

Name _____

Address_____

City _____

State/County_____ Zip Code_____

Preface

PIONEER settlement is a durable research theme in American geography, and the processes and patterns of frontier expansion continue to raise intriguing and perplexing questions. For the cultural geographer in particular, the implications to be drawn from the association of new life with new land suggest some challenging problems. In the present work, a variant form of pioneer settlement—the foreign agricultural colony—serves as a medium in the search for insights into the complex workings of the cultural variable in man - land relationships.

The study is focused upon changes that inevitably occur as behavioral cues imported by immigrant pioneers prove inadequate in the confrontation with a new and presumably unfamiliar milieu. Facts have been gathered, ordered, and interpreted for an assessment of the assumption that changes in geographically relevant elements of culture—that is, those involved in organization of the environment—leave tangible traces in the landscape. The cultural landscape of pioneer settlements provides the essential evidence for the isolation of instances of cultural conservatism and change and the identification and analysis of the processes these reflect.

The Japanese colony of La Colmena in central-eastern Paraguay offered many advantages for such a study. Among ethnic groups pioneering in Paraguay, the Japanese appear to represent the greatest divergence in culture from the native population. Since the contrast is particularly pronounced in approaches to land occupance, material evidence of Japanese tradition stands out in considerable relief. In addition, the colony site was far removed from previous centers of colonization and hence from extraneous cultural influences.

Analysis of relationships between cultural and geographic phenomena is simplified by circumstances surrounding the evolution of the settlement. From 1936 when the colony was established to 1955, La Colmena was the only nucleus of Japanese settlement in Paraguay. Until 1940, colonists remained isolated from Japan by distance, and with the outbreak of World War II all contact was severed. In 1955 Paraguay again opened the door to Japanese pioneers, but they settled in other parts of the country. New pioneer ventures did not materially contribute to re-establishment of cultural ties between the original colonists and their homeland, and without reinforcements the Japanese have been submerged, at least in terms of numbers, by the growth of the local native population. Thus, in La Colmena there has been little to interfere with direct cultural reactions to native environment, native traditions, and the pressures of pioneering.

In applying the study of cultural geography to Japanese pioneer settlement, at least three fundamental conceptual difficulties were encountered.

First, underlying assumptions rest in part upon an early anthropological axiom: the search for basic principles will most likely be rewarded in the study of peoples whose existence is untainted by the complexities inherent in modern, technologically oriented cultures. On the pioneer fringe, life is fairly elemental, and cultural processes are undoubtedly stripped of some of their complex variables. However, the fundamental error remains— what seems simple is only relatively so; what appears to be typical is more likely to be unique; because specific cultures, regardless of apparent simplicity, are merely the composite of a broad spectrum of individual behaviors, principles emerge only as gross generalizations that are difficult to refine by numerical or other currently popular techniques of analysis.

Second, because acculturation is an essential element of pioneer experience, any attempt to unravel the complex threads of cultural interchange presupposes an intimate familiarity with the participating cultures. Unfortunately, this is an ideal more often acknowledged than attained, and the present example is no exception. For Paraguay, two or three published works offer the only recent ethnological data. A synthesis of these materials and such personal observations as could be gathered in the process of field-work are incorporated in the description of the milieu that provides the matrix for pioneer reactions. Clearly, however, much remains to be learned.

My own firsthand familiarity with Japanese culture is limited to a year's residence in that country as a member of the U.S. Armed Forces—an experience that hardly constitutes a sound basis for cultural insights. There is, however, an enormous body of literature and, because it is readily available, no survey of prewar Japanese culture is included here. In preparation for this study I have attempted to absorb as much as possible from works in pertinent fields, with emphasis of necessity upon those published in English. The present problem is viewed as essentially a field exercise, in which the pioneer landscape provides the basic facts and observation the principal means of integration and interpretation.

Third, by the nature of their interests, cultural geographers are inevitably lured beyond the ordinarily prescribed confines of their parent discipline. The concept of culture itself is both the product and cornerstone of anthropology, and to decipher and apply its principles, traditional boundaries must be crossed. Furthermore, any given culture is a composite whole, the individual parts of which are functionally interrelated. Hence, isolation of recognizably geographic elements from their total behavioral context is methodologically unsound. If explanations for a specific artifact in the landscape lead from labor cooperation via kinship to religion, the cultural geographer is obliged to follow.

In Paraguay, an effort was made to visit as many as possible of the settlements owing their origin to foreign agricultural colonization. These trips provided useful comparative data and were of inestimable value in enlarging perspectives to include all aspects and problems of pioneer settlement. In addition, because colonies are scattered throughout the country, the various journeys in search of pioneers offered an opportunity to examine first-hand many of the basic elements of Paraguayan land and culture.

Data on La Colmena were gathered during two periods of residence in the colony—from May 4 to May 28, and from November 13 to November 20, 1958. During these intervals all zones of the settlement were visited, and 10 of the approximately 100 Japanese farmers were chosen for intensive study. Additional information was acquired from colony leaders and Japanese diplomatic and immigration officials in Asunción. Several visits were also made to newer Japanese settlements elsewhere in Paraguay.

To acknowledge the many great and small instances of kindness, hospitality, and cooperation that made this study possible is a frustrating task. It is never possible to credit all who contribute, and to lump all of them together under a collective expression of appreciation, no matter how sincere, seems woefully inadequate. To the following I would like to offer my particular gratitude, and to those unnamed I would like to offer my assurances that all contributions were greatly valued.

To the colonists of La Colmena, whose cooperation was freely given and graced with many acts of kindness, my deepest appreciation is offered; to Shonosuke Oka, head of the Japanese Cultural Association; to Fujio Moriya, general manager of the Cooperative; to A. Tomita, colony surveyor; and to Namio Mitue, a successful farmer, a particular debt is owed.

To Susumu Shokawa for translating an enormous volume of Japanese source materials, I am especially grateful.

To the Foreign Field Research Program, administered by the Division of Earth Sciences, National Academy of Sciences - National Research Council, under sponsorship of the Geography Branch, Office of Naval Research, Contract N00014-67-A-0244-0001 [formerly Contract Nonr-2300(09)], NR 389-105, for underwriting the study; to Dr. Henry Bruman, Dr. Joseph Spencer, and Dr. Benjamin Thomas for invaluable criticism during preparation of the manuscript; to Dr. Harry Coffin, who offered valuable criticism and whose hand-lettering graces the maps, I am also deeply grateful.

My wife, Margaret, whose companionship, patience, endurance, and skill were essential ingredients in everything from initial packing to preparation of the final manuscript, contributed inestimably to the successful completion of this study.

Although this work is the product of many minds and hands, all responsibility for errors, omissions, and inaccuracies rests solely with the author.

Contents

Figures

Tables

CHAPTER 1

The Physical Fundament in Eastern Paraguay

P ARAGUAY, in its gross physical patterns, is a land of simplicity. This is not to imply that knowledge of the country is easily acquired and essentially complete or that the Paraguayan landscape is without challenges, either in interpretation or human occupance. But from maps as well as from published descriptions it is observable that the elements of physical geography readily lend themselves to generalization.

The Paraguay River forms a remarkably precise boundary between two essentially different types of country. To the west lies the vast aggrading plain of the Gran Chaco with its meandering and shifting drainage, its paradoxical aspects of flood and drought, and its dense mat of subtropical thorn scrub that gives way grudgingly to palm savanna along broad drainage courses of the past and present. East of the river the monotony of the flat alluvial landscape is rapidly replaced by topographic variability, and rainfall increases in amount and reliability.

Greater physical variety in eastern Paraguay does not alter the premise of basic simplicity. In spite of reduction in the scale of observation to this region, which contains one third of the country's surface area, environmental contrasts, with the possible exception of those involving climate, may be sketched in broad outlines without appreciable loss of critical detail. Little or no

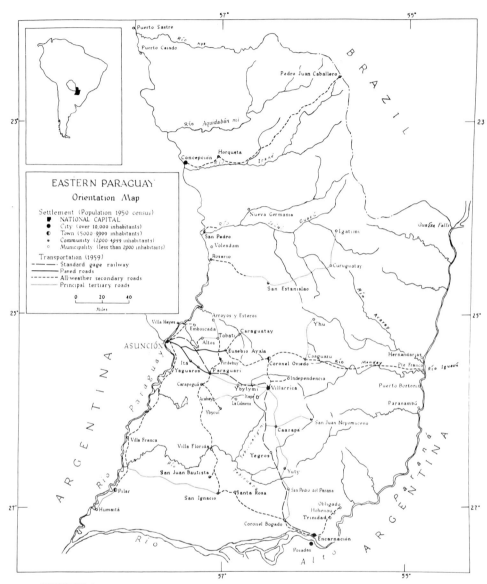

FIGURE 1

attempt is made here to pry deeply into processes. The intent is merely to examine the general habitat qualities of the region in order to identify problems and prospects involved in the varying interpretations of indigenous and introduced cultures (Figure 1).

LANDFORMS AND HYDROGRAPHY

Eastern Paraguay is characterized by low elevation and modest relief.[1]* The region's lowest point, at the confluence of the Paraná and Paraguay Rivers, is a mere 180 feet above sea level, and although two isolated hills have summits slightly above 2,000 feet, at least 80 percent of the area is under 1,000-feet elevation (Figure 2). Spacious plains, broad level-floored valleys, and extensive low plateaus predominate; their surfaces are flat to gently rolling with local relief rarely exceeding 100 feet.

Yet in spite of the subdued aspect of much of the landscape, slopes tend to be surprisingly abrupt; uplands rise suddenly from valley floors or alluvial plains to broad surfaces of moderate relief. Few such areas are elevated more than 50 to 60 feet above surrounding lowlands. East of Asunción, however, in the Central Hill Belt, and particularly along the western margin of the Paraná Plateau, changes in elevation of several hundred feet or more are accomplished within short horizontal distances. These latter uplands, boldly marking the horizon from considerable distances, foster the illusion that rugged terrain is of more importance to Paraguay than is warranted by its actual elevation or areal extent.

The essential similarity of surface forms over large areas permits the subdivision of eastern Paraguay into five physiographic units (Figure 3). The three largest regions—the Ñeembucú Plain, the Central Lowland, and the Paraná Plateau—are also the most uniform. The smaller units—the Northwestern Upland and the Central Hill Belt—contain a greater variety of forms, but differences in degree outweigh those of kind.

---

* Superscript numbers which appear throughout the text refer to Chapter notes, beginning on p. 177.

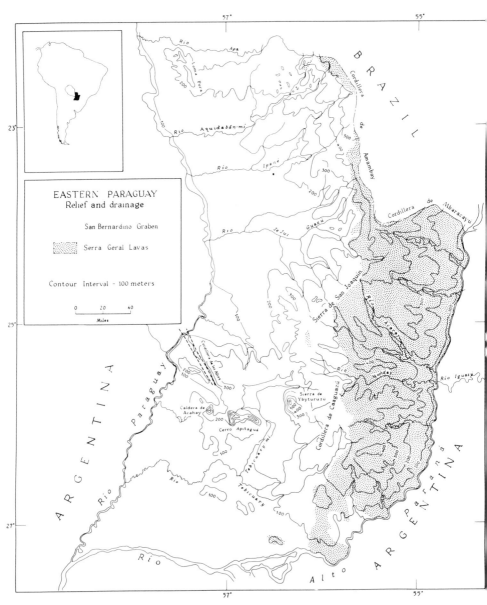

FIGURE 2

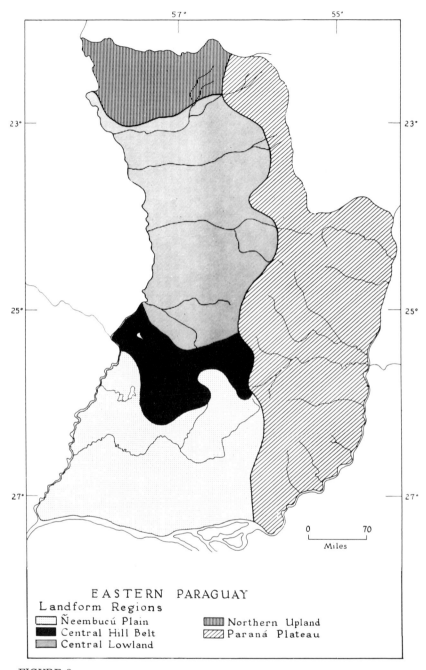

EASTERN   PARAGUAY
Landform Regions
☐ Ñeembucú Plain   ▦ Northern Upland
■ Central Hill Belt   ▨ Paraná Plateau
▦ Central Lowland

FIGURE 3

The Ñeembucú Plain

The extreme southwestern portion of Paraguay is a vast alluvial plain covering nearly 10,000 square miles. This feature is part of a large alluvial lowland that extends well beyond Paraguayan borders but for purposes of this study the plain is delimited on the south and west by the Alto Paraná and Paraguay Rivers. The northern and eastern boundaries, which roughly coincide with the 100-meter contour, are irregular; long fingers of the Central Hill Belt penetrate the region from the north, and eastward the plain terminates abruptly along the western edge of the Paraná Plateau.

With the exception of several small isolated areas near its center, the plain is deeply mantled with alluvium.[2] The topographic anomalies near the plain's center are formed by broad rounded swells that rise 100 feet or more above the sea of alluvium. These uplands, which provide sites for communities evolved from the Jesuit mission centers of San Juan Bautista, San Ignacio, and Santa Rosa, represent weathered remnants of sandstone outliers of the Paraná Plateau 60 miles to the east.

Variations in elevation on the plain itself are difficult to detect. The regional slope is to the west and southwest, but the gradient is readily obscured by gentle undulations that characterize the surface. Drainage is the most reliable indicator of topographic irregularity; after heavy rains, water ponds for long periods in the boggy, roughly circular shallow depressions. Occasionally a house and a few planted trees mark the crests of broad swells or islas (islands) that usually escape inundation.

The Central Hill Belt

In the irregular band of uplands extending eastward and southeastward from Asunción to the Paraná Plateau, topographic texture contrasts significantly with the prevailing level aspect of the country (Figure 4). Nearly flat surfaces are not entirely lacking, but hills dominate the landscape, and their varied forms and alignments indicate a complicated morphologic history.

Topographic irregularities begin at the Paraguay River in the vicinity of Asunción.[3] Within the city, several hill crests stand

FIGURE 4

Topographic texture in the Central Hill Belt (looking north from the summit of the Cerro Apitaguá). In the south-central part of the region, small volcanic cones cover the largely basaltic plains in background.

300 feet or more above the river. However, toward the interior, to the east and southeast, interfluves and valleys broaden sufficiently to give an impression of more subdued topography. Twenty miles east of Asunción the rolling uplands drop steeply into a narrow structural trench, the northern end of which is occupied by Lake Ypacaraí (Figure 5).

The Ypacaraí graben, which extends 40 miles southeastward from its junction with the Paraguay River, determines the topographic alignment of an important segment of the Central Hill Belt. The western border is unimposing, but near the town of Paraguarí it terminates in cliffs that rise several hundred feet above the settlement. Across the nearly level boggy floor of the trench, an average distance of 2.5 miles, the Cordillera de los Altos ascends rapidly to a crest more than 1,000 feet above sea level. From the summit the rolling surface slopes gradually toward the north and east.

East of the graben and its flanking hills, undulating terrain of

FIGURE 5

The Ypacaraí graben, looking west from the Cordillera de los Altos;
shallow Lake Ypacaraí, which occupies the northwestern end of the trench,
is visible to left.

modest elevation and relative relief continues to characterize the
landscape. East of Villarrica, however, the Sierra de Ybyturuzú
rises sharply to its narrow crest at an elevation of 2,300 feet.
This hill is surrounded by an extensive area of dissected upland.
In the German colony of Independencia, located on the upland,
steeply rounded slopes descend abruptly as much as 200 feet to
the beds of small creeks that have already removed much of the
former surface.

The southern segment of the Central Hill Belt consists of
smaller isolated eminences, which vary in form depending upon
their geologic origin. The most conspicuous relief elements are
products of local vulcanism that appear to be more or less contem-
poraneous with the extrusion of the Paraná Plateau lavas. South
and east of Paraguarí a low, nearly level plain has been formed
upon basaltic flows. Around its margins are numerous small
volcanic cones and dikes, but several larger volcanic piles form
the most prominent features of the landscape (Figure 6). The
Acahay caldera is approximately 3 miles in diameter and rises

FIGURE 6

Small volcanic cones on basaltic plain south of Paraguarí. In right background is the Caldera de Acahay. Vegetation is typical of heavily grazed lowland campo.

900 feet above the surrounding plain. The Cerro Apitaguá, 15 miles to the west, is an even larger volcanic mass consisting of several linear ridges reaching more than 2,000 feet above sea level. To the south, ancient crystalline and paleozoic sedimentary rocks are exposed in the form of rounded eminences, which decrease in size and elevation as they merge with the Ñeembucú Plain near the Tebicuary River.

The Central Lowland

North of the Central Hill Belt, low elevation and relief again characterize the surface. Eastward from the Paraguay River over a 7,500-square-mile area between the Aquidabán River on the north and the Arroyo Yhaguy on the south the land slopes gently upward to the western edge of the Paraná Plateau. Near the Paraguay River the country resembles that of Ñeembucú.

Further inland the surface is interrupted by isolated, irregularly shaped eminences with broad tops of low relative relief. These uplands, which vary in area from a few acres to several square miles, rise steeply 20 to 60 feet above the alluvium deposited by the Paraguay and its eastern tributaries. They are apparently deeply weathered remnants of bodies of rock related to the geology farther east. Their forested surfaces, which project above the grass-covered alluvium, are referred to locally as islas de monte ("wooded islands") and their margins, termed costas ("coasts") are favored as settlement sites (Figure 7).[4]

Within 20 miles of the Paraguay River the islas de monte increase in area and elevation and begin to lose their insular aspect as they merge to form a continuous upland surface. Alluvial lowlands are reduced to level-floored valleys that accommodate the westward-flowing Paraguay tributaries. However, although valley plains are no longer the dominant landscape feature, they extend eastward almost to the Paraná Plateau as broad expanses of poorly drained land. These extensive marshy areas are the

FIGURE 7

Small "wooded islands" in the Central Lowland near the Mennonite colony of Volendam (Mbopicuá).

principal impediments to establishment of road connections between central and northern Paraguay.

The Northern Uplands

North of the Aquidabán River the surface forms, except in the north and west, resemble an extensive plateau elevated approximately 600 feet above sea level and 250 to 300 feet above the Central Lowlands to the south. The plateau, formed primarily on ancient crystalline and metamorphic rocks, consists of broad rounded interfluves and wide-floored valleys into which streams are lightly incised. Rounded knobs of resistant rock stand conspicuously 100 feet or so above the general level, but the overall aspect is one of greatly subdued relief.

Near the center of the region a low range of hills has been up-faulted along a line that runs southwest from the Río Apa for a distance of 35 miles. The southern half, known as Loma Porá, is flat topped like the surrounding plateau, above which it projects some 180 feet. Near Paraguay's northern border, however, the block has been raised several hundred feet higher and dissected into a hill land of conical peaks, serrated ridges, and steep slopes. West of Loma Porá, metamorphosed limestone is folded into several 600-foot-high hills; however, the effects of solution are confined to the banks of the Paraguay River.

The Paraná Plateau

Basaltic lavas of the Paraná Plateau extend well into eastern Paraguay. In the north the indentation of the Brazilian border excludes from Paraguay all but the rugged western edge of the Plateau. However, with the eastward turn of the border to the Alto Paraná River near the 24° Parallel, the uplands penetrate 90 miles into the eastern part of the country to cover approximately one third of its surface.

In Paraguay the extrusives and the Plateau surface are not coextensive. The Plateau border, including a zone averaging 10 miles wide, is composed of the thick series of red sandstones that apparently underlie most of the basalt. A large inlier of the same sandstone outcrops along the Alto Paraná near the Jesuit ruins of Jesús and Trinidad (for which it provided the building materials) and the German colony of Hohenau.

Approached from the west the edge of the Plateau rises with a scarplike face that extends unbroken from the Brazilian border to the Alto Paraná River near Encarnación. The scarp is compact except in the extreme north where small tabular hills have been detached by erosion. In the north also it is highest, descending from 1,500 feet above sea level near Pedro Juan Caballero to approximately 600 feet at the southern extreme. The prominence of the western plateau border has invited the attachment of numerous names. It is identified variously on maps as the Cordillera de Amambay, the Cordillera de Mbaracayú, the Sierra de Joaquín, and the Cordillera de Caaguazú. In local usage, however, these names, along with others, are applied indiscriminately.

Since the Plateau slopes moderately to the east as well as to the south, its western edge is also its highest point. The surface itself, despite interesting topographic minutiae described by Carnier, is remarkably uniform. Broad interfluves are separated by narrow V-shaped valleys into which the Alto Paraná tributaries have been incised. The Paraguayan segment of the Plateau terminates sharply in the deep trench carved by the Alto Paraná; the Paraguayan bank seems particularly abrupt, often standing in vertical cliffs rising 50 feet or more above the river.

Patterns of drainage in eastern Paraguay reflect the essential flatness of much of the terrain. On maps, marshland is indicated for much of the western third of the region. Lowlands in the Paraguay watershed are usually poorly drained and subject to occasional inundation, but the extent of marshland depends largely upon the time of observation. After heavy rains, vast areas of the Ñeembucú Plain and the Central Lowland are often flooded. Claypans beneath the surface prevent absorption of flood waters, and low gradients inhibit runoff. In addition, Paraguay River tributaries are inclined to overflow their banks when swollen with rainwater, which cannot be discharged because of concomitant rises in the level of the parent stream. However, permanent marshes are few. Only in the largest depressions such as those occupied by the broad, shallow lakes of Ypacaraí and Ypoá is the land perennially boggy, and even these lakes have fluvial connections with the Paraguay.

The Paraguay River is the master stream of a fluvial network that drains the western two thirds of eastern Paraguay. Flowing southward from Mato Grosso and the vast swampy Gran Pantanal, it forms the western border of the region for 380 miles between the Apa River and the junction with the Alto Paraná. Throughout the river's length the gradient is less than 5 inches per mile, and numerous islands, meander scars, and oxbow lakes attest to recurrent shifts of channel.

Except for short distances where the Northern Uplands and the Central Hill Belt reach the river, banks are low, alternately sloping gently away from the stream bed or rising abruptly as steep cutbanks. Along that part of the river personally traversed, from Villeta to Concepción, steep cutbanks carved from clayey alluvium predominate, particularly on the east. The plains adjacent to the east, although apparently deeply mantled with alluvial deposits, do not seem to be actively aggrading, and classic floodplain forms do not appear to be conspicuously developed.

The flow of the Paraguay is subject to moderate seasonal and annual variations.[5] According to Schuster, the mean annual change in level at Asunción is approximately 5 feet, and absolute maximum is about 23 feet.[6] Stream velocity exhibits similar variations—seasonally owing to changes in volume of water, and locally because of constrictions in the channel. Seldom, however, does the current exceed 3 miles per hour.

Major Paraguay tributaries are miniatures of the parent stream. Their headwaters descend rapidly from the western edge of the Paraná Plateau, but upon reaching the lowlands, valleys broaden, gradients diminish, and the sluggish streams meander westward to join the Paraguay at grade. Most tributaries appear to be lightly incised in their alluvial valleys. At low water, vertical banks rise 5 to 20 feet above the beds, but after heavy rains these miniature gorges rapidly fill and occasionally overflow to inundate adjacent lowlands.

The Paraguay is navigable, with limitations from the Paraná junction to Corumbá, a distance of more than 1,000 miles. Most years, boats with a draft of 7 feet ascend the river as far as Concepción without difficulty. During the rainy season, medium-sized ocean vessels reach Asunción, but tortuous bends, constantly shifting sandbars, and the threat of stranding by a drop in water level make such visits rare. Most tributaries are navigable for small boats and barges, but traffic is negligible.

The Alto Paraná River forms the border of eastern Paraguay for 500 miles between the Paraguay and the Guaíra Falls. At these cataracts the Alto Paraná plunges 300 feet in several stages into a narrow gorge. From this point southward the river is confined by vertical and near-vertical walls that decline in elevation from 300 feet above the river to less than 100 feet near the great westward bend that carries the river past Encarnación.

Within its gorge the current averages more than 10 miles per hour. Seasonal variations in rainfall throughout the watershed and the narrowing of the river course as it enters the gorge combine to cause marked fluctuations in water level in remarkably short periods of time. At low water, exposed edges of basaltic flow produce rapids in the bed of the river. Within 24 hours, however, floods totally unrelated to local meteorological conditions may raise the water level 50 feet or more.[7]

Near Encarnación the Alto Paraná leaves its confining, lava-walled gorge and turns westward for a distance of 180 miles to join the Paraná. In the process the river widens to a maximum of 18 miles. Its channel is braided, with at least one intervening island reaching 200 square miles in area. With increased breadth the river accommodates seasonal fluctuations in volume with less pronounced modifications in level or velocity, and the current is reduced to 6 miles per hour.

Tributaries to the Alto Paraná differ markedly from those flowing into the Paraguay. Heavier rainfall and the nature of the surface geology combine to produce a far more intricate drainage network on the plateau. At least 16 rivers and many shorter creeks enter the parent stream between Encarnación and Guaíra Falls. They are incised in the plateau surface and follow unusually sinuous courses carved along myriad joints in the basalt. Most of the larger streams enter the Alto Paraná River gorge in steplike falls. The cataracts of Río Monday are impressive, though modest compared to those of the Iguazú.

The navigational utility of the Alto Paraná, like that of the Paraguay, is strongly conditioned by seasonal variations in volume of water. In the summer the river is usually deep enough everywhere to permit boats of 10-foot draft to reach Guaíra. Even during the rainy season, however, the water level can drop sufficiently to expose basaltic "reefs."[8] For several months during the dry season a bedrock sill between larger islands in the lower course is brought within 3 feet of the surface, effectively severing communications between the upper river and Buenos Aires. The swift current of the Alto Paraná poses an additional handicap. Alto Paraná tributaries are unnavigable because of cataracts at or near their junction with the parent stream.

CLIMATE

The climate of eastern Paraguay has consistently caused writers to extend themselves in the search for superlatives, and one authority has recently been moved to nominate the country a "natural paradise."[9] In terms of dispassionate statistical values the climate is perhaps best generalized as humid subtropical. However, such a characterization obscures significant details that make this region a paradise with reservations.

The lack of pronounced topographic barriers in central South America places Paraguay in the path of air masses migrating unimpeded and little modified from two source regions of widely divergent characteristics. During the high sun period, moist tropical air from Amazonas extends southward as far as the estuary of the Río de la Plata. In winter, pamperos (frequent outpourings of polar air) move through the Paraná-Paraguay depression, bringing freezing temperatures as far north as central Mato Grosso. Throughout the year the daily weather is conditioned by the movement of these air masses and is frequently disturbed by the passage of fronts marking the zone of contact between them.

Nature of Available Data

Meteorological data currently available for eastern Paraguay provide an inadequate basis for precise description or analysis. Before 1900 most travelers recorded only subjective impressions of the climate.[10] In 1919 Mangels[11] published the results of 23 years' observations in Asunción, and a few years later Bertoni[12] published meteorological data gathered intermittently during more than 30 years' residence along the Alto Paraná. These two sets of weather records form the basis for almost all subsequent accounts.[13]

In 1933 the Paraguayan government established the Dirección de meteorología to systematize the gathering of weather data throughout the country, but there is no complete record available of the activities of this agency or its various predecessors. Moreover, since its founding, the Dirección has not functioned with consistent efficiency, and instrument data for most localities other than the capital are short, incomplete, and of unknown reliability.

TABLE 1

Availability of Climatic Data for Eastern Paraguay

Rainfall and Temperature	No. of Years	Rainfall Only	No. of Years
Asunción	More than 50	Concepción	5
Encarnación	12	Cosme	7
Horqueta	10	Nueva Germania	6
Itacurubí	7	Puerto Sastre	8
La Colmena	8	San Salvador	10
Pilar	10		
Presidente Franco	13		
Puerto Bertoni	14		
Puerto Casado	7		
Villarrica	13		

Principal sources: Clayton and Clayton (1927; reprinted 1944). Clayton and Clayton (1947). Fariña Sanchez (Apr., 1946). Knock (1930). Tirado Sulsona, MS records from files of Servicio Técnico Interamericano de Cooperación Agrícola (STICA), U.S. Operations Mission to Paraguay—now Agency for International Development. U.S. Dept. of Commerce (1959). U.S. Dept. of Commerce, MS and microfilm records.

Data for 15 stations with records of more than 5 years are available (Table 1, Figure 8); length of record varies from 5 to more than 50 years, and for most stations, years of record seldom coincide. In addition, not all locations have recorded the same weather elements, and there is little consistency in the manner of data presentation. Owing to such limitations, Paraguayan climatic data are not particularly amenable to graphic expression. However, charts have been prepared for six stations with concurrent 11-year records, data from official sources being utilized[14] (Figure 9).

Rainfall

The rainfall of eastern Paraguay is subject to considerable geographic, annual, and seasonal variation. Although the data are contradictory, it appears that no part of the area receives less than 50 inches of rain as an annual average. There is less certainty about maximum values, but apparently the 70-inch isohyet

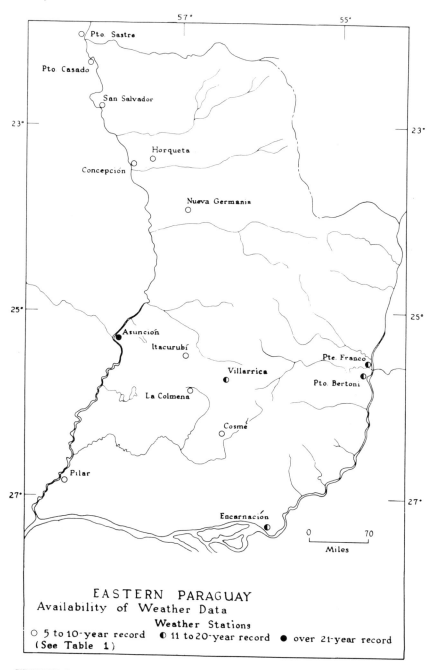

EASTERN PARAGUAY
Availability of Weather Data
Weather Stations
○ 5 to 10-year record   ◐ 11 to 20-year record   ● over 21-year record
(See Table 1)

FIGURE 8

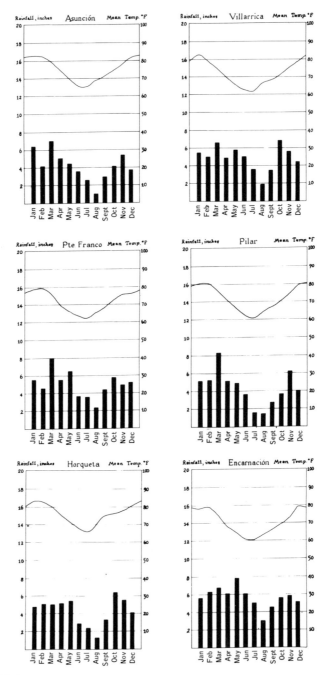

FIGURE 9

Climatic charts, various stations.

lies to the east of Paraguay's eastern border.[15] Differences in
amounts received from north to south are negligible except, perhaps, for the zone adjacent to the Alto Paraná River. Here, Wilhelmy stated, rainfall increases slightly toward the north.[16]
However, the contrast between eastern and western Paraguay is
significant. Stations along the Paraguay River average 50 inches
of rainfall annually, some 10 to 15 inches less than stations along
the Alto Paraná in the same latitudes. According to available
maps the increase eastward is assumed to be regular.[17] Although
there may generally be such an increase, contrasts in amount
are modest enough to be readily obscured by local factors of relief and exposure (La Colmena, 63 inches vs Presidente Franco,
59 inches) or annual and seasonal variations (in 1940, Asunción,
69 inches vs Presidente Franco, 64 inches).

The rainfall regime is characterized by a marked high sun
concentration. At all stations August is the driest month. West
of the Paraná Plateau, August receives less than 2 inches, and
the difference between the driest and wettest months varies from
6 inches to more than 7 inches. Along the Alto Paraná, seasonal
distribution is more equitable; no month receives less than 2.5
inches, and differences between highest and lowest values vary
from 4 to 5 inches. The seasonal position of the wettest month is
variable. All localities show a tendency toward double maxima—
one in spring (October - November) and the second in March—
separated by a usually slight midsummer "rain pause."[18] At four
stations (Asunción, Presidente Franco, Pilar, Encarnación) the
fall maximum is most pronounced; March is the wettest month
except at Encarnación, where the maximum is delayed until May.
Horqueta and Villarrica receive their heaviest precipitation in
October.

These statistical averages, however, obscure pronounced
annual and seasonal variations. In Asunción, for which there is
a nearly complete 70-year record,[19] an absolute minimum of 22
inches was recorded in 1906, yet in 1919, the rainiest year, 82
inches fell. In 38 years, rainfall was below average. Similar variations are noted in Bertoni's records for various localities on
the Paraná Plateau; at Puerto Bertoni 131 inches were recorded
in 1899, but in 1906 only 31 inches fell. Significant variations
also occur in monthly totals. For Asunción only two months
(July, 1933, and August, 1938) are noted as entirely rainless.
Yet August, the driest month, has received as much as 5 inches.
The greatest variation is exhibited by the rainiest month which
in 1892 received 21 inches but in 1928 received barely a trace.

Although Paraguay receives most of its precipitation when tropical air masses predominate, local convection seems to play a minor role. Precipitation more commonly accompanies advancing fronts of cooler air from the south. Pressure gradients between the invading pampero and the resident tropical air are often quite steep, and resultant storms are accompanied by towering cumulus, copious downpours, high winds, and extraordinary displays of electrical phenomena. Such storms are heavily concentrated between October and May but occur at irregular intervals throughout the year. However, winter rains, particularly in the southeast, often appear in the form of prolonged drizzles that are apparently connected with more extensive cyclonic disturbances.

Precipitation occurs infrequently in forms other than rainfall. Snow is mentioned by several authors but is considered by most observers to be wholly unknown.[20] Hail is expectable as a concomitant of thundershowers, but hailstorms are noted as rare by most authorities. Relative humidity is moderate to high, even during winter, and condensation in various forms contributes to available moisture. Fogs are common in topographic depressions in the interior and along the Alto Paraná. Heavy dew is typical of mornings through much of the year. According to Bertoni, dew in the Alto Paraná zone is equivalent to from 7 to 10 inches of rainfall annually.

Temperature*

From October to March, when moist tropical air is dominant in eastern Paraguay, monthly mean temperatures at Asunción are above 75°, and January, the warmest month, has a mean of 84°. Eastward, monthly mean values decline slightly: Villarrica has above 70° for the period and 80.2° for the warmest month; Presidente Franco has 78.9° for the warmest month (February). During this period daytime temperatures above 100° are common, and the daily range seldom exceeds 20°. However, the entire region is subject to frequent incursions of cool air from the south. In the normal summer sequence of daily weather, clear skies prevail for a week or 10 days, during which temperature and

* All values are in degrees Fahrenheit unless otherwise noted.

relative humidity climb steadily toward their maximum values. Just as the heat seemingly nears the limit of human endurance, storm clouds, moving rapidly from the south, indicate the approach of the pampero. Temperature changes associated with the passage of these cold fronts are characteristically sudden and marked; within minutes the temperature may drop 25° or more. The passage of the storm requires only a few hours, and in the following days temperatures again begin their gradual ascent toward maximum values.

April and September are months of transition; maximum temperatures average comfortably below midsummer values, and minima may dip below freezing. However, both months usually exhibit temperatures analagous to one of the principal "seasons," and hence they appear to be variable extensions of summer or winter rather than periods of unique weather.

The winter period, from May to August, is short and relatively mild. For all stations, July is the coldest month; means decline eastward from 65.2° at Asunción to 62.4° on the Paraná Plateau. The lowest minimum (12°) has been reported in the Alto Paraná zone,[21] but apparently no place in eastern Paraguay is entirely free from the possibility of frost. As in summer, unseasonable weather frequently interrupts the normal march of temperature. Villarrica, with a mean July maximum of 71°, has recorded mid-winter maxima above 90°.

Statistical generalizations for temperature, like those for rainfall, obscure important variations. Experiences of farmers indicate that microclimatic variations deviate significantly from statistical norms, particularly with respect to critical threshold values for agricultural plants. For example, strong nocturnal cooling during calm winter nights frequently produces killing frosts in topographic depressions. In addition, temperatures are subject to strong annual and seasonal fluctuation. During summer the cold fronts that serve to depress maximum temperatures are undependable, and weeks may pass in which the ascent of daily maxima is totally unhindered. At such times, maxima may exceed 105° for days, and the parched landscape waits in vain for relief in the form of the pampero. The absolute maximum officially recorded in the capital, 107.6°, occurred during one such heat wave in 1934.[22]

Winter temperatures are similarly unpredictable. According to Mangels, the number of days with temperatures below 32° in the vicinity of the capital ranged from 3 to 16 yearly.[23] In the interior, contrasts from year to year are even more pronounced. Some winters are extraordinarily mild with prevailing north winds, and frosts, if they occur at all, are restricted to some of the least favored locations. At the other extreme, deep tongues of polar air have spread over the entire region, bringing subfreezing temperatures to all stations.

Climate and Human Occupance

In rural Paraguay, the persistence of simple agricultural techniques among natives and immigrants has tended to foster a relationship of considerable intimacy between climate and human occupance. The climate is moderate, and on the basis of average conditions there has been no need for distortion in creating an appealing picture for immigration propaganda or travel pamphlets. Yet Paraguay is not without natural hazards for those attempting to live from the soil.

Although winters are usually mild, the threat of frost precludes cultivation of tropical plants, and even with subtropicals there is occasional risk. Coffee, for example, is grown in several parts of the country, but even with close attention to patterns of microclimate, loss by frost is possible.[24] Nor are such native plants as yerba immune to frost damage. In the absence of climatic data, crop selection, particularly for agricultural pioneers, is largely a matter of trial and error, and costly failures are not unknown. Topographic irregularity also invites difficulty. If the survey of parcels for colonization produces a lot that lies almost wholly within a moderate swale, the success of its ultimate owner is highly speculative, at least in terms of crops normally commercialized in Paraguay.

Recurrent droughts also plague Paraguayan agriculture. During the relatively rainless winter, a month or more may pass without precipitation, endangering perennial plantings of coffee, yerba, and tung, as well as long-range field crops such as mandioca. Summer droughts also occur, and because these coincide with the growing season and are accompanied by high temperatures they are more serious. The frequency of such calamities is difficult to determine. In the countryside, memories of specific years of crop failure are hazy, and station records are equally vague. For Asunción, total rainfall has been disastrously deficient during

at least five of the years since 1934. However, total precipitation
is a poor index, because some years with impressive totals have
experienced several consecutive months with little more than a
trace of rain.[25]

Too much rainfall is equally troublesome. Roads are unsurfaced
and generally without bridges, and prolonged rains paralyze the
transportation system. Excessive precipitation is also prejudicial
to several important crops, including cotton and wheat. In addition,
farmers must contend with several other weather hazards. Colonists resident in Paraguay for more than seven years report the
loss of crops to hailstorms. There is disagreement as to whether
tornadoes occur;[26] in any case, steep pressure-gradients accom-
panying cold fronts often produce violent winds that are capable
of doing considerable damage.

VEGETATION

Prior to the turn of the present century only a handful of trained
botanical observers reached Paraguay, and contributions to the
published record were few.[27] Between 1900 and 1920, Hassler
and Chodat[28] published the results of more than 20 years' botanical research in the country, and this work forms the basis of
most subsequent descriptions.[29] The United States aid programs
to Paraguay, established in 1942, have stimulated additional botanical inquiry, but most such work has been confined to cultivated
plants.

Several authors have attempted to generalize the Paraguayan
flora in terms of physiognomic associations and to present their
distribution on maps or in phytogeographic essays.[30] Unfortunately, incomplete botanizing makes such efforts highly speculative, and there is little agreement among authorities on classification, nomenclature, or boundaries. In Figure 10, I have attempted to synthesize the important early works and to add details
based upon aerial photographs and field reconnaissance. However,
boundaries are tentative and subject to correction through intensive phytogeographic field work. Several conspicuous types of
vegetation, including islas de monte, palmares (palm savannas),
and campo alto [upland campo or grasslands, Hochkamp (upland
vegetation) etc.,] by virtue of their small area and scattered
distribution are difficult to show precisely on small-scale maps.

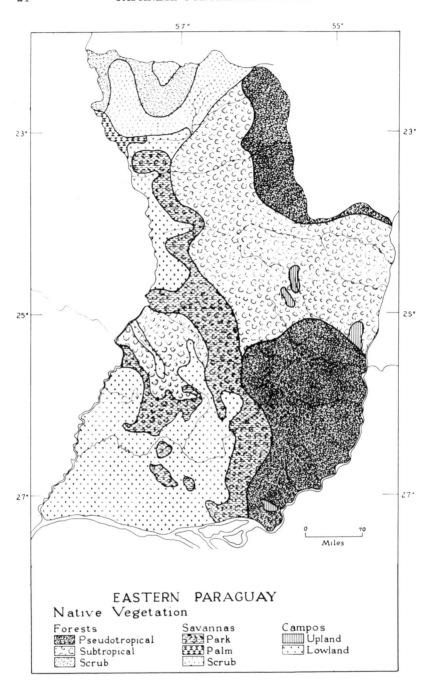

EASTERN PARAGUAY
Native Vegetation

Forests   Savannas   Campos
Pseudotropical   Park   Upland
Subtropical   Palm   Lowland
Scrub   Scrub

FIGURE 10

Forest

Approximately one half of eastern Paraguay is covered by dense
and often imposing forest. Forests reach their maximum development on the Paraná Plateau where they extend almost without in-
terruption across 90 percent of the surface. To the west the forest
gradually deteriorates with the decrease in rainfall, and the oc-
currence of tree growth is controlled by topography and drainage.
In the Central Hill Belt, forest accompanies the upland areas as
far west as the Paraguay River. North of this region, as uplands
grade into isolated islas, the forest shares the landscape with
intervening herbaceous associations in the form of park savanna.
Where drainage is poor, as in the vast Ñeembucú Plain, forests
are replaced by other forms of vegetation except for narrow
galaria ribbons.

The Paraguayan forest presents difficulties in classification
and nomenclature. The descriptive term "subtropical semidecid-
uous" is usually applied to such forests, yet in spite of seasonality
in temperature and precipitation, in Paraguay the forest retains
many essentially tropical characteristics. Furthermore, regional
variations in ecological conditions produce marked contrasts in
forest aspect throughout the country; some authors have isolated
as many as seven forest types. However, the critical distinction
involves increases in environmental limitations that produce concomitant deterioration in the forest from near tropical in the most
favored locations to less exuberant manifestations elsewhere.
On this basis it is possible to recognize and roughly map three
forest associations.

1. THE PSEUDOTROPICAL FOREST   The most nearly tropical
of Paraguay's forests spreads northward across the Paraná
Plateau from Hohenau to the Acaray River—an area that coincides
with the country's maximum annual rainfall. To the north the
forest continues to the Brazilian border but becomes more xeric
as rainfall diminishes in amount and reliability. Along the Cordillera de Amambay in the extreme northeast the forest again
thickens to near-tropical proportions. Similar though slightly
degraded forest extends into the Central Hill Belt as far west as
Villarrica and occurs in isolated moist ravines less than 40 miles
from the Paraguay River.

In these areas tree growth is both dense and luxuriant (Figure 11).

FIGURE 11

Clearing in dense pseudotropical forest of the Paraná Plateau (Colonia
Hohenau). Trees average 80 feet in height; trunks of felled trees average
between 3 and 4 feet in diameter. Lianas and philodendron roots hang
vertically from tree crowns.

Forest giants reach heights of 120 feet or more, but the complete
canopy averages somewhat less than 100 feet, and although trees
of varying growth habit are present, stories are difficult to
discern. According to a recent survey the average forest acre
contains approximately 110 trees.[31] With the exception of a small
grove of Paraná pine (Araucaria angustifolia) near the Alto Paraná
River port of Paranambú,[32] the forest consists entirely of broad-
leaved species, some of which are deciduous. Leaf drop varies
with locale, but in general the predominant aspect is green at
all seasons. Only in spring when a few deciduous species such
as the lapacho (Tecoma spp.) burst spectacularly into bloom is
seasonal rhythm conspicuous.

In terms of species composition the forest is heterogeneous.
In sample strips Hamill has encountered 120 different species,
with those of the family Leguminosae predominating.[33] An average acre contains some 15 or 20 species. However, on the basis
of Hamill's samples, some 20 species account for three quarters
of the total forest volume, and isolated pockets dominated by one

or two species are not uncommon, as in the case of the yerbales (Ilex paraguayensis).

In spite of the dense canopy, undergrowth is usually moderately well developed and includes giant tree ferns, tropical Piperaceae, broad-leaved Gramineae, giant and small bamboos (Gadua, Chusquea, Bambusa), and bromeliads, especially the Anana macrodontes. Lianas and other climbing plants are conspicuous, and epiphytic Orchidaceae and Cactaceae are common. Of the many palms native to Paraguay only the pindo (Cocos romanzoffiana) is found occasionally in the pseudotropical forest.

2. THE SUBTROPICAL FOREST   North of the Acaray River on the Paraná Plateau and in the western portion of the Central Hill Belt, forest continues to dominate the landscape. In the most favored locations it is difficult to distinguish from the near-tropical growth. Over most of these areas, however, environmental limitations have produced less luxuriant growth of slightly different composition. Although heterogeneous species distribution remains generally characteristic, the tendency toward single species dominance is more marked; it is in this region that the most important concentrations of wild yerba are located. Trees are lower and more widely spaced, and in the undergrowth moisture-loving tropicals give way to brush and scrub. Lianas and other climbing plants continue to play an important role; palms are more conspicuous, and various Euphorbia enter the association. The more xeric nature of the habitat is indicated by an increase in the number of succulents including Cereus, Opuntia, and various Bromeliaceae. On the drier margins and on rocky or sandy soils, typical scrub forest plants (Prosopis, Mimosa) have pioneered.

3. THE SCRUB FOREST   Scrub forest, known locally as matorral, espinarillo, capuera, is dominant in the Chaco and is also widely distributed in the eastern part of the country. However, in eastern Paraguay its distribution is difficult to map accurately. Shrubby growth occurs widely as second growth after forest clearing but is usually transitory. Small isolated patches of scrub also favor areas of specialized edaphic conditions; for example, espinarillo, a tangle of thorny shrubs and low trees interspersed with succulents and densely interwoven with tough lianas, seems to favor alkaline soils.

Only in the vicinity of the Apa River, which has been invaded by floristic elements of the Chaco and Mato Grosso, does native thorn forest cover large areas. Here stunted trees (<u>Mimosa</u>, <u>Tecoma</u>, etc.), heavily interspersed with palms (<u>Geonoma</u>, <u>Coper-nica</u>, dwarf <u>Cocos</u>, etc.) and densely compacted shrubs (<u>Mimosa</u>, <u>Bauhinia</u>, <u>Anona</u>, Compositae, etc.) are the typical vegetation form. Even here, however, masses of thorn bush are usually detached from one another and, with intervening grasslands, produce "bush savanna."

Campo

The classification and nomenclature of tropical grasslands and grass - woody associations continue to trouble plant geographers. In order to describe and map the major herbaceous elements of Paraguayan flora, I have followed several authorities as well as local usage in restricting "campo" to grasslands in which woody growth is absent or inconspicuous and applying "savanna" to associations in which herbaceous and woody elements are more or less codominant.

Over extensive areas of eastern Paraguay, Gramineae are the dominant and often the only conspicuous floristic element. Grasslands vary in aspect and composition, depending upon details of habitat and the degree to which man has interfered with ecological processes. In general, however, two types may be distinguished on the basis of gross environmental contrasts: lowland campo (<u>campo bajo</u>) occupies poorly drained alluvial lowlands; upland campo (<u>campo alto</u>) occurs in small patches in well-drained uplands throughout the eastern portion of the country.

1. LOWLAND CAMPO   West of the Paraná Plateau the association between poor drainage and grassland is very close. In isolated marshy spots a form of tangled scrubby <u>matorral</u> is found, but in the main the broad alluvial flats adjacent to stream courses and the vast, gently rolling alluvial plains in the southwest are covered by relatively pure grassland (Figure 6, p. 9). In areas not heavily grazed, tall coarse bunch-grasses predominate (<u>Paspulum</u>, <u>Panicum</u>, <u>Andropogon</u>), often in association with Cyperaceae.[34] Where flooding is regular and prolonged, tall reed, cane, and saw grasses (including <u>paja colorada</u>, <u>Paspulum quadrifarum</u>, the universal roof-thatching material) grow in dense masses. In less hygrophilic situations, bunch-grasses seldom attain a

height of more than four feet, and individual clumps are more
widely spaced; Cyperaceae decline in importance, and shrubby
Compositae are not uncommon.

2. UPLAND CAMPO   The distribution of upland grasslands is
as yet impossible to map accurately. Patches up to several square
miles in area occur randomly in the Central Hill Belt, in the southern Paraná Plateau near Encarnación and Hohenau, and east of
Coronel Oviedo near the Mennonite colonies of Sommerfeld and
Bergthal. However, other small areas are scattered throughout
the uplands of northern and central Paraguay.[35]
    Upland campo is apparently more uniform in composition and
poorer in variety than its lowland counterpart. Short, primarily
annual seed grasses predominate, particularly Andropogon,
Paspulum, Eragrostis, and Stipa. Fiebrig notes that native rhizomatous and stoloniferous grasses are few, yet many well-drained
campos are carpeted with an evergreen sod of such grasses.[36]
More or less herbaceous Leguminosae (Crotalaria) are typical
of this association, but Compositae are far more numerous. Various guavas (Psidium spp.) favor protected campo margins.

                        Savanna

Regions in which herbaceous and woody plants share the landscape
on more or less equal terms are confined primarily to the central-
west and extreme north. The park savannas of the central zone
are composed of islas de monte separated by campo-covered alluvial flats (Figure 7, p. 10). Floristically, campo elements differ
little from the lowland grasslands previously described. Forest
occupying the irregular islands resembles more lush manifestations of the subtropical forest with which it shares many species
in common. The most striking characteristic of islas de monte is
the spiny thicket of caraguatá (Bromelia balansae) with which they
are invariably ringed.
    Bush savanna is found only north of the Aquidabán River where
in many areas the landscape resembles the campo cerrado of
Brazil. Low trees and shrubs, singly or in clumps, alternate with
grassy patches in an almost infinite variety of combinations.
Among grasses, most of which are less than 3 feet high, Aristida
is the predominant genus, but Andropogon, Elyonurus, Trachypogon,

Chloris, and Briza are noted as representative.[37] The growth
habit of trees reflects the xeric nature of the habitat; most of
them are less than 20 feet tall, with broad canopies and crooked
trunks. Palms are conspicuous, including typical scrub forest
species. The myriad shrubs, which exhibit a wide variety of stat-
ure and foliage characteristics, include Anona and Mimosa among
the most common genera. Succulents are surprisingly rare; Fiebrig and Rojas note the curious lack of the terrestrial bromeliads
caraguatá and yvirá, which are common elsewhere in eastern
Paraguay, and the paucity of Cactaceae, represented here by only
a few species of Echinocactus.

Palms are conspicuous elements of the landscape in eastern
Paraguay, but rarely are they natural dominants over large areas.
However, along the Aquidabán River, Chaco floristic elements in
the form of palmares have pioneered the marshy lands east of
the Paraguay. Here, patches of the common Chaco palm Caranday[38] tower over the tall bunch-grasses along the broad alluvial
valleys of the river's major tributaries.

The Human Factor in Paraguayan Flora

It is hardly possible to describe the native vegetation of eastern
Paraguay without recognition of man's role in altering its composition and distribution. The particular uses that various cultures
have found for the native flora are detailed in subsequent chapters.
But considering the length of human occupance of the region and
the long history of agricultural exploitation, it is probable that
no part of the landscape remains undisturbed.

Cultivation has its greatest impact upon the forest association.
Until relatively recently, farming was restricted by primitive
technology to forested land, and clearing has been a continuous
activity since well before the Columbian discoveries. Within a
60-mile radius of the capital, most forest has been converted
permanently to farm land. Throughout the remainder of the country, with the exception of the Paraná Plateau, there is hardly a
patch of forest that is not ringed with agricultural clearings.
Paraguayan farmers tend to shun forest interiors, but even here,
remnant Indian groups, though greatly reduced in number, continue
to practice shifting cultivation. Whether or not deforestation has
altered the Paraguayan climate, as some authorities claim, the

effects upon vegetation have been pronounced. Outside the densely settled central region, where cultivation is apt to be migratory, large areas of forest have been converted to scrub. In the north and northwest particularly, where tall-tree forest is close to its ecological margins, second growth is slow and seldom total because recovery is usually interrupted by renewed clearing.

In the deforested central region, the invasion of the native mbocayá palm (Acrocomia totai) is noteworthy. This palm, which "follows the plow," according to a Paraguayan proverb, rapidly pioneers agricultural plots, a process tolerated if not encouraged by Paraguayan farmers because in their view the utility of the tree far outweighs its nuisance value (Figure 39, p. 139). In many fields the mbocayá stands in compact, pseudoregular masses, as if planted, thereby greatly inhibiting cultivation. The role of man in the spread and distribution of this palm is significant. The mbocayá is apparently a poor competitor and if left to its own devices will eventually disappear. Where found in noncultivated land it is usually a reliable "old field" indicator.[39]

Forests have also provided raw materials for numerous extractive industries that have experienced varying intensities of exploitation. Charcoal is the major domestic and industrial fuel, and forests are being sacrificed to supply ever-increasing needs. Timber is much used locally and has long been one of Paraguay's chief export items. Selective logging has all but removed five or six of the most merchantable species from accessible areas. Gathering activities have also contributed to alteration of the forest. Exploitation of wild yerba dates from pre-Columbian times and more recently has been responsible for the seasonal migration deep into the forest of hundreds of gatherers and their families.

Herbaceous associations have also been profoundly altered. Indeed, Bertoni goes so far as to suggest that the Paraguayan campo, whatever its origins, represents a wholly artificial flora.[40] The impact of aboriginal land use upon the grasslands is unknown,[41] but livestock has been intimately associated with Paraguayan life for almost 400 years, and it is difficult to imagine a sizable grass-covered area in the country that has not been extensively grazed. Burning to improve forage quality and to destroy ticks is a custom several centuries old in this part of South America,[42] and foreign colonists have readily adopted the practice. In lowland campo, pressures of grazing and burning are reflected in the diminution of tall cane and reed grasses, which are being replaced by lower-growing species. This change is viewed as favorable by ranchers, but many of the more successful herbaceous competitors are apparently of markedly inferior forage quality. In upland campos, which are unprotected by a deep humus layer or by moist depressions, repeated firing has produced even greater changes. The number of tropical grasses in general and annual species in particular has declined perceptibly, and hardier southern genera (Stipa, Eragrostis) have invaded these campos. In addition, the Leguminosae have been largely replaced by less palatable Compositae.

Concurrent with these disturbances have come inadvertent as well as overt plant introductions that have escaped man's control, becoming thoroughly integrated with native plant communities. The case of the orange is illustrative. Various citrus fruits were introduced by the Spaniards, and the orange rapidly became acclimatized. Before the 19th century it spread throughout the forest of eastern Paraguay and has been reported from adjacent parts of Brazil and Argentina.[43] In its "wild" state the orange has apparently deteriorated genetically into a number of subtypes, many with primitive attributes, including large thorns and fruit with flavor varying from mildly astringent to wholly unpalatable.

Attempts to improve pastures have resulted in the introduction to Paraguay of numerous Gramineae. Most of the stoloniferous and rhizomatous grasses that are currently widespread have been brought from elsewhere, as indicated by their nonspecific and inconsistently applied names (Brazil grass, Pará grass, Jesuit grass, etc.). Some of these have spread beyond control, particularly in the vicinity of settlements, where they have become established in plazas, common pastures, streets, and yards. These and similar escapes are usually beneficial because they improve range capability. However, several have proved decidedly prejudicial. Johnson grass (Sorghum halpense) and Bermuda grass (Cynodon dactylon) provide forage, but because of relatively simple agricultural techniques their rapid expansion into agricultural lands in the central and southeast portions of the country has led to considerable difficulty and even to abandonment of otherwise productive farms.[44]

SOILS

Soils of eastern Paraguay, like the climate, are much fabled but little studied. Until very recently knowledge of soils was confined to optimistic exaggerations of fertility in published accounts, and even today their cultivation, both by pioneers and natives, is based upon practical experience largely incorporated in folk rules of thumb. Since 1948, data gathered according to principles of modern soil technology have slowly begun to accumulate.

More than 70 percent of eastern Paraguay is elevated sufficiently to escape periodic inundation. Over much of this surface relative relief is moderate, and long exposure to processes of weathering has produced a residual soil mantle of extraordinary depth. Surface exposures of bedrock are rare, and wells from 15 to 50 feet in depth seldom reach the bottom of the weathered zone. Residual soils, where personally observed in wells, road cuts, and excavations, appear to lack distinct profiles (Figure 12). In general, they are red in color, sandy in texture, and acid in reaction (pH 5.3 to 5.8 for the most extensive soil series). Laboratory analyses indicate that most of these soils are low in nitrogen, organic matter, and exchangeable bases. Apparently also, they are characteristically lacking in many essential trace elements.

In the most recent survey,[45] areal variation in residual soils is considered to reflect differences in parent material. On this basis they have been divided into several series which correspond roughly, and not always consistently, to surface geology (Figure 13). Three of these series (Asunción, Alto Paraná, and Independencia) cover more than 90 percent of the area occupied by residual soils. The others are limited in distribution and commonly offer severe handicaps to cultivation.

The residual soils in the Asunción series cover almost 40 percent of eastern Paraguay. They predominate in a zone 90 miles wide, from the Aquidabán River and the Brazilian border south to the Tebicuary. They are also the chief soils in the densely settled agricultural region surrounding the capital. These areas are underlain by sandstone, and soils weathered from it are inclined to be droughty and impoverished.

Alto Paraná soils, developed from basaltic lavas, cover approximately 25 percent of eastern Paraguay. They are similar to related soils in Brazil and northwestern Argentina; however, those personally observed lack the characteristic purplish coloration

FIGURE 12

Digging a fire pit for yerba drying shed (bar-
bacua) exposes uniform soil structure to considerable depth. Author's wife is 5 feet
6 inches tall (Colonia Sudecia in central
eastern Paraguay).

of the famous terra roxa. These soils are considered to be the
country's best in terms of agricultural productivity. But, although
their structure and drainage characteristics are superior, they
possess significant deficiencies in exchangeable bases.

Independencia soils mantle about 10 percent of the surface of
eastern Paraguay, occupying large irregular patches from Villarrica north to the Brazilian border and smaller areas near Asunción. Derived chiefly from indurated sandstone, these soils are
relatively shallow with poor water-holding capacity. Analysis
has shown them to be the poorest of all residual soils in organic
matter and available nutrients.

Transported soils occur along drainage courses and in topographic depressions subject to periodic flooding. The largest
such area is the broad Ñeembucú Plain. Another large area

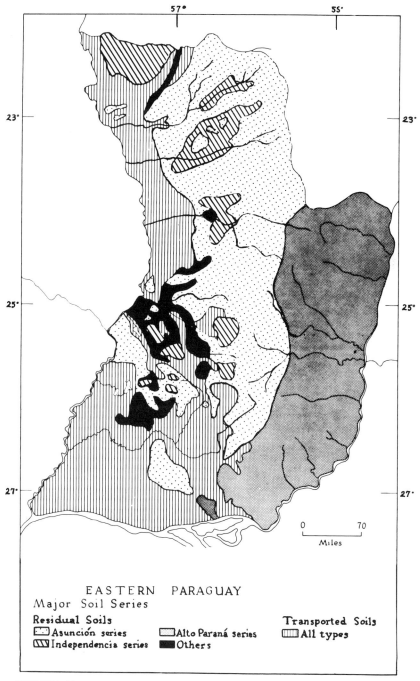

EASTERN   PARAGUAY
Major Soil Series
Residual Soils   Transported Soils
Asunción series   Alto Paraná series   All types
Independencia series   Others

FIGURE 13

borders the Paraguay River in the Central Lowland, extending inland an average distance of 20 miles, but reaching eastward along major tributaries as far as 60 miles. Soil characteristics vary depending upon the lithology of surrounding uplands and details of local relief, but most are similar in utilization potential. Soils of the poorly drained areas are typically shallow and sandy and are underlain by mottled, plastic, impervious clays or clayey sands.

As a medium for agriculture, the residual soils are generally adequate and are well suited to the various forms of shifting cultivation commonly practiced. However, stable agricultural settlement based upon the cultivation of permanent fields requires recognition of inherent soil deficiencies. The sandy texture of most soils indicates low water-holding capacities. Even during years with abundant rainfall, shallow-rooted field crops on sandy phases of Asunción and Independencia soils are subject to drought, and the problem is compounded during recurrent droughts that characterize the regional climate.

The presence of imposing forest on all but the poorest residual soils fosters an illusion of limitless and indestructible productivity to which foreign pioneers and native Paraguayans have easily fallen prey. For several years after clearing, most forest soils yield magnificently irrespective of parent material. However, with many crops, especially those common to commercial farming, soils are rapidly depleted with continued cultivation.

Although nutrient deficiencies, whether inherent in Paraguayan soils or induced by sustained farming, can be overcome, primitive agricultural techniques and attitudes among Paraguayans include only vague notions of soil management. For immigrant pioneers possessing superior agricultural technology the economics of Paraguayan agriculture make the use of chemical additives impractical and offer little stimulus for improvement of production. Under these circumstances colonists faced with declining yields have tended to abandon whatever predilection for soil conservation they brought to Paraguay. The most common substitute is the native view that uncleared forest is capital reserve to be put to the plow in small amounts only as needed. Money, time, and energy are not invested in improvements; rather, because land and labor remain relatively cheap, profits are expended in acquisition of new forest for projected expansion of plantations, as a hedge against the future, or even to build an estate, because the original homestead, denuded of forest and cropped for years, is usually hardly worth passing on to heirs.

Paraguay's transported soils offer even greater obstacles to agricultural utilization. They are shunned by the bulk of the farming population and for the most part are left to support coarse native bunch-grasses that nourish most of the eastern Paraguayan cattle. Near the Paraguay River where soils are deeper and abundant water is available, rice is successfully grown. For such a crop the impervious clay subsoil is an asset rather than a liability. However, rice growing requires capital investments beyond the means of most peasants and pioneers.

FAUNA

The role of faunal elements in patterns of human occupance in eastern Paraguay has been steadily declining. Even relict Indian groups of the Paraná Plateau, who still consider themselves primarily hunters, have come to rely more upon the digging stick and less upon the bow and snare. In all other elements of the population there is an increasing tendency to pursue the native wild life as a sport rather than as an essential element of the food quest or as an economic resource. Furthermore, the jaguar, tapir, deer, wild pig, capybara, and many lesser creatures have declined in numbers as they have been forced to relinquish more and more of their domain to man. Only fishing seems to retain something of its original interest. But even this resource, which apparently fluctuates little in terms of its original abundance, creates activity surprisingly casual and often no more than recreational.

In addition, there are negative attributes inherent in the Paraguayan fauna which must be counted among the natural hazards of the region. To Paraguayans armed with familiarity bred of long experience these hazards are merely part of the natural order, but to foreign agricultural pioneers they present challenges in adjustment and even in survival.

A catalog of Paraguayan pests would prove extensive indeed. The most vexing to foreigners belong to the insect world. Several varieties of anopheline mosquitoes have been responsible for occasional outbreaks of malarial fevers; in the early 1900's the newly established German colony of Hohenau lost approximately half of its members to malaria, and the entire enterprise almost collapsed.[46] But the majority of Paraguay's insects are more bothersome than fatal. The mbareguí,[47] a biting gnat of the Paraná forest, may produce severe and uncomfortable swelling lasting a week or more; at best its bite causes itching welts that, if scratched, easily become infected. The pique,[48] a minute louselike insect, lays its eggs in the layers of skin of the feet, producing intensely itching blisters that become painfully crippling if not properly cared for. The ura, a fly larva that grows to the length of an inch or more while feeding beneath the skin of its host, regularly infests cattle and other domestic animals in great numbers, but man is also a target. Ticks abound and descend from the foliage by the hundreds when disturbed.

Personal assaults from insect fauna are insignificant in comparison with the damage inflicted upon crops. All domesticated plants native to the country have a complex of pests and diseases, and plants introduced from elsewhere soon acquire one. Of general concern, however, is the isaú, a voracious leaf-cutting ant that occasionally invades plantations. The mound-building termite favors well-drained pastures and campo but is not above constructing a tall cemented clay nest in a farm plot from which it is almost impossible to remove. Plagues of locusts occasionally blight large regions; three times between 1936 and 1955 the Japanese of La Colmena lost most of their crops to locusts. Crop damage is inflicted by other faunal forms, particularly monkeys and the many varieties of native parrot.

Against all such hazards, whether to health or to livelihood, protection is possible, but the means are seldom available in Paraguay, much less in the country's isolated pioneer settlements. Even if they could be provided, costs would be prohibitive to most immigrant colonists, whose cash yield from agriculture is low. Thus foreign settlers have been pushed toward the Paraguayan philosophy of accepting Nature's more hostile manifestations and, in the process, have become susceptible to Paraguayan experience and lore in such matters.

CHAPTER 2

Cultural Geographic Survey of Rural Paraguay

FOR more than 400 years Paraguay has provided the background for the amalgamation of two distinct populations which, through compromise and exchange, have produced a composite race and welded a national culture. To immigrant colonists this national culture functions as a reservoir of solutions to unfamiliar problems. More importantly, it provides a firmly established social, economic, and political construct within which foreign pioneers must contrive to fit.

In order to characterize this cultural configuration, it is necessary to survey the gross patterns of Paraguayan demography, economy, and politics. However, the emphasis here is upon the rural Paraguayan, his mode of land occupance, and the cultural equipment that gives these activities their distinctive stamp.[1] Although cities currently are experiencing renewed growth, the essence of Paraguay is still the campaña—the rural countryside in which most Paraguayans live and function. Furthermore, it is the rural culture pattern, often in its most primitive form, to which immigrant settlers have been most freely exposed.

POPULATION

Number and Distribution

The first modern census of Paraguayan population was concluded in 1950.[2] Considering the inherent difficulties, the results should be regarded as indicative rather than precise. However, the data provide a reasonable basis for demographic and geographic analysis of population patterns, and many prior assumptions may now be documented, modified, or discarded.

The census enumerates 1,400,000 Paraguayans living within the country's borders.[3] The often-made generalization that Paraguayans are concentrated in a densely settled zone near the capital is borne out by the data; more than 95 percent live between the Paraguay and Alto Paraná Rivers, and approximately 60 percent reside in the Central Hill Belt (Figure 14).

The census also graphically confirms the rural quality of Paraguay's population. The country's 151 municipalidades[4] contain approximately one third of the total. Asunción, with a population of 201,000, is the only urban agglomeration of consequence. Only three other cities (Villarrica, Concepción, and Encarnación) have populations in excess of 10,000. More than 100 communities have 2,000 inhabitants or fewer, and the majority number fewer than 1,000. It is probable that census figures do not precisely reflect the current urban - rural ratio. Around most communities but outside their legal limits are clustered numerous dwellings sheltering people whose principal concern is the adjacent town. Furthermore, the trend toward urbanization is apparently increasing although not everywhere with equal intensity. The capital is perhaps the most rapidly expanding city, but Encarnación also has experienced considerable growth.

Surprisingly, the geographic instability usually associated with Paraguayans is not confirmed by the statistics. In published works the Paraguayan is often described as nomadic. The common assumption is that because few Paraguayans own land they have little attachment to any specific locality and are often forced to pursue opportunity where they find it. However, census data indicate that in all but one department, at least 70 percent of the residents were born in the department in which they were censused. In the central zone, percentages of more than 90 are noted,

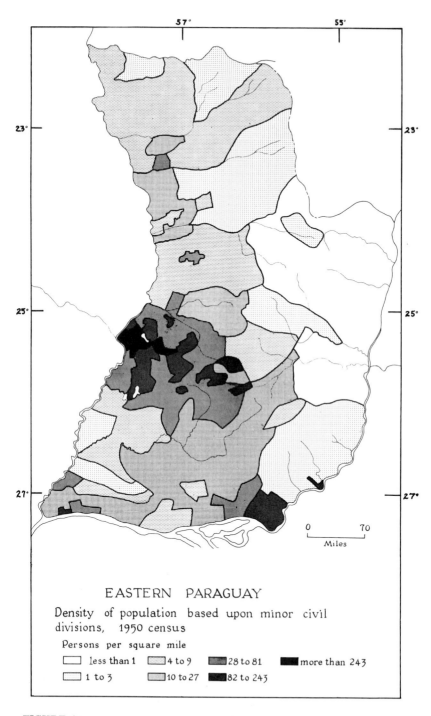

EASTERN PARAGUAY

Density of population based upon minor civil divisions, 1950 census

Persons per square mile

□ less than 1   □ 4 to 9   ▨ 28 to 81   ■ more than 243
□ 1 to 3   □ 10 to 27 ■ 82 to 243

FIGURE 14

but even in isolated and less developed northern departments geographic stability is marked.[5]

Composition

A persistent misconception in the literature of many fields is that Paraguay is one of the predominantly Indian countries of Latin America. Until recently the extraordinary viability of the Guaraní language, along with a fairly primitive culture, invited the assumption that the Paraguayan aborigines had, like the historic Chinese, vanquished their conquerors by absorption. Thanks largely to the work of the Services it is clear that racially, and for the most part culturally, the average Paraguayan can in no sense be considered an Indian.[6]

The primary ingredients in the Paraguayan racial makeup are limited to the Colonial Spanish and the native Guaraní Indians. Negro slaves were introduced by the Spaniards, but their presence is no longer apparent.[7] The blending of introduced and native races has been extremely thorough. Remnant groups of Guaraní Indians, estimated to number about 8,000,[8] persist in the Paraná forests. Paraguayans of undiluted Spanish ancestry are probably no less rare, and European and Oriental immigration since 1880 has not been sufficient to alter the mestizo character of the population.

The relative contributions of Spanish and Indian to current racial patterns are not easily determined. The total number of Spaniards entering Paraguay during the Colonial period is thought to have been small. However, to anyone encountering a large cross section of the Paraguayan people it is obvious that the Spaniards overcame their numerical disadvantage. There is a spectrum in physiognomy from obviously Indian to obviously not, but the non-Indian appearance definitely predominates.[9]

At the risk of belaboring an already much overworked point, it is cogent to consider the imbalance in the sex ratio that is commonly attributed to Paraguay because such a phenomenon, if it existed, would undoubtedly play a significant role in acculturation of immigrant pioneers. The fable that Paraguay is a land of women has proved remarkably persistent. However, the 1950 census indicates a normal sex ratio; furthermore, whether there has ever been a serious imbalance in the numerical relation between the sexes is open to speculation.[10]

ORIGINS OF PARAGUAYAN NATIONAL CULTURE

In outlining the general configuration of Paraguayan culture and identifying the significant processes of its formation, valuable spadework has been done by the Services. In an excellent monograph on early Spanish - Guaraní relationships, Service clearly illuminates the adaptive changes in Spanish social and administrative institutions that gave a unique flavor to cultural contacts in this portion of South America.[11] The first European settlers in Paraguay numbered fewer than 400, and subsequent reinforcements from Spain never amounted to more than a trickle. Yet through polygynous association with Indian women a large mestizo population rapidly emerged. By 1600, individuals of mixed breed apparently far outnumbered Spaniards.[12] In the process of miscegenation the conquerors became enmeshed in Guaraní kinship structure and were able to assert control and satisfy labor demands within this framework. Later introduction of the encomienda did not appreciably alter this basic relationship, and the protective mechanisms built into the system for preservation of the aborigines and their culture failed to function.

Paraguay's isolation and lack of sources of ready wealth further conditioned Indian servitude and had a profound effect upon the social order. The colonial economy was reduced for the most part to a subsistence level, and the hacienda phenomenon so typical of other Hispanic American regions did not materialize. In addition, the Guaraní possessed no sophisticated political or social organization which the Spaniards could manipulate from the top.[13]

The termination of the Colonial period did not necessarily halt these early formative processes, which reduced Paraguayans to a relatively homogeneous population with an overwhelmingly Hispanic "cast" to their culture. On the contrary, the extraordinary early dictatorships served to intensify the country's isolation and to further reduce racial and cultural contrasts. After the War of the Triple Alliance (1865 - 1870), Paraguay began gradually to participate in world commerce and to accept foreign immigrants. However, adventures in these fields were not notably successful and their impact upon native culture was slight. The Chaco War (1932 - 1935) renewed world interest in the region but prostrated the national economy and nullified much of what little progress had been achieved in incorporating the majority

of the population into an integrated commercial system with international involvements.

During World War II, the United States assumed an active
interest in the affairs of Paraguay that continues in the U.S. Foreign Aid Program. It is too early to assess the degree to which
United States financial and technical aid have functioned as forces
of cultural change. The rapid growth of Asunción since World
War II suggests that changes are occurring, and although much
of rural Paraguay is still excluded by poor communication, roads
are reaching farther into the campaña to bring more and more
Paraguayans into the orbit of urban-commercial activity centered
in the capital.

The cultural base upon which these changes are taking place
is described by the Services in their study of Tobatí, a "typical"
Paraguayan rural community. The Services' findings indicate
that present culture patterns crystallized early in the Colonial
period and have evolved without significant outside influences.
The model was Hispanic, and much of the modified colonial configuration remains. Although at least some local culture must
represent an intimate fusion of Hispanic with aboriginal elements,
little direct evidence of Guaraní heritage could be found:

> Despite the slowness of change since the colonial period, we find that
> in rural Paraguay today there are virtually no Guaraní culture traits
> surviving, other than language. There are, to be sure, certain native
> foods, and perhaps a few culinary customs still in existence, but native
> items of this sort survived everywhere to some extent, even in North
> America. . . . But a careful analysis of even such things as mythology,
> folklore, superstitions, and folk medicine failed to reveal anything of
> certain Guarani origin.[14]

The single, undeniably Guaraní, survival is the language.[15]
To state with Steward that "most Paraguayans are bilingual" is
to grossly underestimate if not misunderstand the role of the
Guaraní tongue.[16] Guaraní is still spoken as the first and preferred language by an overwhelming majority of the population
and as the only language by a surprising number of Paraguayans.
According to the 1950 census almost half of those older than
three years of age spoke only Guaraní.[17] Most of the remainder
are noted as "bilingual," but it is readily observable that most
rural Paraguayans are more comfortable in the aboriginal tongue
and retreat to the security and familiarity of it whenever possible.

The prevalence of Guaraní has been the source of some difficulty to immigrant pioneers and hence is of more than passing

interest to the present work. Guaraní has no counterpart in
European or Asiatic languages and has proved difficult to master
for those born and reared elsewhere. Since most colonies are
located in isolated rural areas, the linguistic barrier has been
immediate, almost total, and persistent. The conflicts and frus-
trations rooted in this inability to communicate would require far
more space to analyze fully; however, there seems to be little
question that the Guaraní language has both direct and indirect
consequences for cultural change among pioneers. Lack of a
common language has obviously reduced the possibilities for
interchange and has functioned selectively in those elements of
native behavior to which colonists have been exposed. In addition,
the fact that Guaraní is an aboriginal tongue has tended to reinforce feelings of superiority among pioneers, and has led them
to exaggerate and dwell upon the cultural gulf that separates them
from most Paraguayans.

SETTLEMENT AND STRUCTURE PATTERNS

Settlement in rural Paraguay is characterized by rural dispersion. The small communities scattered throughout the eastern
part of the country are focuses of commercial, administrative,
and religious activities, but for most Paraguayans association
with them is infrequent and casual. Most peasants are engaged
at least for part of the year in agriculture and prefer to reside
on the land they cultivate. Even when seeking off-farm employment, peasants usually gravitate to farms or forests.

In larger cities and in communities close to the capital, the
pattern of regular markets is common but by no means universal,
and in more isolated rural contexts the town market is even less
important. Meat, yerba maté, and caña (the native alcoholic drink
made from sugarcane), the principal items of native purchase,
are easily acquired throughout the countryside—meat at licensed
farmsteads where the owner provides slaughtering facilities, and
caña at the "sign of the white flag" where residents augment
their income by converting their dwellings into impromptu bars.
Yerba maté, galletas (biscuits), and other processed foods, as
well as dry goods and utensils, may be found in boliches (small
neighborhood stores).[18]

Residence sites are conditioned largely by agricultural considerations. To Paraguayan farmers, forest is the only practical medium for cultivation. Rarely, however, do they settle deep in the forest totally out of touch with neighbors. The most favored sites are the costas where forest and campo meet. Here there is land for planting and pasture for work animals. In addition, such sites are usually nearest to water. In the central region, where the agricultural landscape has spread to permanently consume most of the forested land, the costa pattern no longer obtains.

Rural dwellings vary within a narrow range of basic styles and materials. The standard rural residence consists of two structures: the dwelling proper and a small cooking shed (Figure 15). Dwellings are rectangular with one end enclosed by walls to form a single room and the other protected only by the roof. The roof is supported by three horizontal poles—one at the ridge and two at each of the lower edges—which rest in vertical crotched logs sunk into the ground at both ends of the structure. Roof pitch is moderate, and overhang is slight. The open end is gabled, but that part sheltering the enclosed room is just as likely to be conical, with the enclosing wall semicircular (Figure 16).

FIGURE 15

A Paraguayan rancho, consisting of a main dwelling and adjacent cooking shed (La Colmena).

FIGURE 16

Typical peasant rancho under construction. Thatching of the roof will complete the structure. In background clearing, cotton is planted amidst smoldering forest debris (Potrero Alto, Cerro Apitaguá).

Roofs are thatched with native grasses and occasionally with palm fronds. Thatching is keyed with mud to a lashed branch grid (Figure 17), but the use of wire is becoming common. Thatch is seldom more than four inches thick and is neatly trimmed at the roof edge.

Floors are of packed earth held in place with staked logs. Walls are constructed from split palm-logs driven vertically into the ground and lashed together with vine or rope. Over these a branch lattice is placed, and mud plaster is applied both inside and out. Adobe brick is known but not generally used. Windows are usually absent, and entrance to the single room is by a narrow door that opens upon the sheltered porch.

The cooking structure is small and simple—a crude gabled roof with three or four enclosing walls that are unplastered so that smoke can escape from the chinks. The fire is built on the floor and ringed by stones for support of the ubiquitous three-legged iron pot. A beehive-shaped mud or brick oven is placed in the yard (Figure 18).

A second rural type of house is constructed of the same materials but is a simple rectangular one-room structure with gables at

FIGURE 17

Mennonite colonists thatching a shed in Paraguayan fashion. Thatch bundles, with squared ends dipped in mud, are thrown to the man on the roof (Colonia Friesland).

FIGURE 18

Outdoor "beehive" oven. Although made of brick, its form is identical with those made of mud (La Colmena).

both ends. A ramada near the front door provides a porch. The ramada in Paraguay, as elsewhere in Spanish America, is a flat framework of woven branches supported by four corner-posts and commonly covered by climbing plants.[19]

A third but far less common type differs from others only in plan. It is longer, in order to accommodate two rooms separated by an open breezeway leading to the rear of the structure. Such dwellings are typical of cattle estancias, but they occur also in agricultural and even urban situations.

There are many variations upon these basic themes, depending upon the attitudes and affluence of the inhabitants and whether or not the structures are intended for permanent occupance. Among poorer elements of the population, structures, easily constructed and readily abandoned, reflect the utter simplicity and lack of care in their building. The most expendable structures may take the form of primitive palm-thatch lean-tos still found among relict Indian groups (Figure 19). More often they are crude imi-

FIGURE 19

Palm-thatch lean-to, built by Mbyá-Guaraní Indians. It consists of two branch-and-thatch panels attached to a short ridge pole. A single panel, propped against a convenient tree, also suffices (near Colonia Hohenau).

tations of basic rural styles. But even on relatively permanent
structures, plastering is often omitted. In the vicinity of the capital a far greater air of stability and permanence is reflected in
structures; dwellings are neatly plastered and whitewashed.

Basic rural styles have infiltrated towns to a certain extent,
but urban dwellings differ in several important respects. Residences with one or two rooms are rectangular in plan but vary
in roof styles, one having the ridge off center with an abbreviated
front slope, the other with the ridge coincident with the front of
the house and the roof sloping steeply to the rear (Figure 20).
In towns there is likely to be considerable architectural variation;
Spanish Colonial buildings are occasionally preserved beside new

FIGURE 20

House type common in rural communities throughout eastern Paraguay.
Cooking shed is attached at rear (La Colmena).

structures embodying patterns emanating from Asunción. In towns also, brick, tile, and cement are featured in building patterns.

Both in town and in the countryside, yards are apt to be fenced against marauding livestock. The size of the fenced area varies greatly but is usually about one third of an acre. Around dwellings, bare earth is sprinkled and swept regularly; ornamental flowers and fruit trees are often planted, and yards are commonly carpeted with close-cropped forage grasses. Fences are of barbed wire when the owner can afford it, but more often they are constructed of posts to which two or three rows of horizontal poles have been lashed. The Paraguayan gate consists of two posts at opposite sides of the opening. Into each post three holes have been bored to receive the poles that close the opening.

For most of the rural population, house furnishings are starkly simple. Common to almost all homesteads are the large log mortar for grinding maize and a tree-fork stand for the round-bottomed olla in which drinking water is fetched and kept. Gourd containers, often with woven holders, are also in common use. Houses wholly without other furniture are not unknown, but several additional items are widespread. Sleeping arrangements include the hammock (which is now used largely while traveling or as a crib), a low frame bed with rawhide webbing, or simply an animal skin placed on the earthen floor. Crudely fashioned chairs and tables are kept for hospitality, but an older form of stool, a few inches high with the seat in the form of a V, is common. An old trunk or battered suitcase for family belongings completes the furnishings. In towns a wide variety of utensils as well as decorative furnishings are present but most of the rural populace does without them. The household "santo," a nook in which religious images and family photographs are kept, is also more common in towns than in country dwellings.

LIVELIHOOD PATTERNS

The basis of life in rural Paraguay is overwhelmingly agrarian. In 1950 the "economically active" segment of the rural population numbered 341,000 of which nearly 70 percent were employed in farming or ranching.[20] Furthermore, many Paraguayans in business and the professions have vested interests in farms or ranches, and laborers, artisans, and others often engage in agriculture coincident with other employment. Thus, outside the capital it is difficult to encounter a Paraguayan who is totally unfamiliar with native farming technology.

Until relatively recently the nature of Paraguayan agriculture could only be subjectively determined. However, in 1942 a United States aid program was inaugurated with an agricultural census of the entire country.[21] Like the census of population, the results should be considered tentative rather than definitive, but they provide a quantitative framework for analysis and a statistical standard against which commonly held assumptions can be measured.

Land Occupance and Tenure

The agricultural landscape in eastern Paraguay is dominated by small farms. The agricultural census enumerated 94,500 agricultural units (chacras) encompassing 3.8 million acres.[22] About one half of this land is included in the 2 percent of the farms containing more than 250 acres. However, most of these large holdings are in the Chaco or in other sparsely settled zones. Although some cultivation is practiced on such estates, it is incidental to ranching activities. Nearly 70 percent of the farms contained less than 20 acres, and 50 percent proved to have less than 12 acres.[23]

The scope of individual peasant enterprise is even smaller than the statistics indicate. In the central region, farms average 13 acres, but the area actually under cultivation averages less than 5 acres. As Paraguayan farmers devote a large part of their agricultural energies to subsistence, the individual contribution to the nation's commerce is minuscule.

To some extent size, area under cultivation, and even shape of farms are dependent upon accessibility to the capital. A survey conducted near Asunción indicates that where daily or weekly contact with the capital is possible, average farm size increases to 15 acres, and cultivated area per farm expands to twice the general average.[24] Here also, major roads have influenced farm layout. The advantage of road frontage is apparent in the continual narrowing of rural properties through subdivision by inheritance or sale; strips of land no wider than 100 yards and a mile or more in length are not unusual. However, even in the densely settled zone there are areas without ready access to urban markets, and farms with three acres or less under cultivation are common. Without arterial roads to condition alignment, farm patterns show little conscious effort at regularity.

In Paraguay few peasants own the land they cultivate. However, the imbalance between landed and landless does not stem directly from Colonial latifundia. Before 1865 some large estates developed. However, in the War of the Triple Alliance many landed families disappeared, and cadastral records were lost. In the postwar period, all land without certified title became public domain. In 1885 financial difficulties induced the government to dispose of public lands, and under laws permitting unrestricted sale the wholesale alienation of the public domain was accomplished by 1900. As few Paraguayans possessed the necessary capital, most of the land was purchased by foreign interests.[25]

After 1900, further sale of public land was prohibited, and the agrarian law of 1940, which, with modifications, remains in effect, recaptured some of the public patrimony by redefinition and expropriation. This law also contained provision for redistribution of land to peasants, but land reforms have not materially altered patterns of ownership. Of the 94,500 farms for which ownership characteristics are reported, only 15,000 were held by title, and half of these were larger than the typical peasant chacra.[26] In 1944 Lesser calculated that not more than 2.5 percent of the Paraguayan people owned land, and recent estimates indicate that there has been little change since then.[27]

Although most Paraguayans are technically landless, their condition and attitudes are rather different from those of peasants in Latin American countries where peón-hacendado relationships have descended more or less intact from the Colonial period. In Paraguay, the lack of title ownership has not necessarily inhibited the evolution of a relatively independent agrarian peasantry. The country's small population has been prevented by wars and emigration from expanding to fill the national territory. Thus, land has always been abundant, and Paraguayans have managed to appropriate enough for their needs in several ways. Small, owner-operated farms numbering about 7,400 are heavily concentrated around the country's urban nuclei and may stem from the subdivision of larger properties by inheritance. Only about 6 percent of the nation's farms are leased according to arrangements that follow no common formula in payment or obligation.

Rural Paraguay's most common form of occupance is squatting.

Approximately 60,000 of the farms enumerated in the census were operated by peasants without title or formal lease.[28] The right to unused land regardless of ownership is assumed by peasants and tacitly recognized by the government as well as by landowners. Squatters invade public lands without interference, but private lands are equally vulnerable. Squatters are potentially valuable to landowners since the squatters generally feel some obligation to contribute their labor to the patrón when called upon.[29] However, squatters are usually more troublesome than useful, and most landowners would probably eject invaders if the legal mechanisms were less costly and more certain of achieving success.

The prevalence of squatter occupance and the tolerance with which it is viewed suggest an undercurrent of indifference to landownership. The origins of this phenomenon are not entirely clear. However, Guaraní culture did not provide strong inclinations toward ownership, and Spanish acquisitiveness for real estate was early tempered by economic realities. According to Azara, agriculture was practiced in 18th-century Paraguay as an alternative to cattle raising,[30] and as neither was particularly remunerative, the Paraguayans do not seem to have associated land with wealth and status. Furthermore, with vast amounts of land available, ownership was never a prerequisite for survival.

In modern Paraguay the tendency to view farming in the context of subsistence rather than economic self-betterment is still characteristic, and conditions militating against strong attachments to the land have not yet been greatly modified. It is probable also that the migratory aspects of traditional farming practice have influenced attitudes toward land tenure.

Whatever the relative significance of these factors, the lack of interest in landownership does not appear to stem from the hopelessness inherent in quasi-feudal patterns common elsewhere in Latin America. Land in Paraguay is not particularly expensive, and, for those with cultural predilections for landownership, its acquisition is not difficult. In addition, government attempts to increase the number of landowners have not been outstandingly successful. A provision in the Agrarian Law permitting the formation of colonies from groups of 20 squatters has seldom been used,[31] and colonies formed from expropriated estates have not been filled with stable farmers anxious to legally secure their attachment to the land. Thus, rural poverty in Paraguay cannot be ascribed simply to landlessness, and agrarian reform is less potent a political force than it is in neighboring countries.[32]

Crops

In rural Paraguay, cultivation is focused upon plants that were characteristic of the pre-Columbian Guaraní and are still basic to the Paraguayan diet. Mandioca (manioc), maize, various beans, and peanuts account for nearly 60 percent of the cultivated land; mandioca (in yield) and maize (in area planted) lead all others in production. Their importance is further emphasized by the number of farmers engaged in producing them. Table 2 lists Paraguay's principal crops in order of the percentage of farms reporting plantings in 1942-1943.

Of the 94,500 chacras listed, 90,500 produced mandioca. Paraguayan mandioca is nonpoisonous. According to informants, three varieties are most common: early maturing azul; concepción, a heavy producer; and señorita, with an intermediate growing season and yield. Mandioca is reproduced by lengths of stalk sufficient to include four or five protruding nodes from which new growth emerges. Two pieces of stalk are laid horizontally in holes 5 or 6 inches deep and about 1 yard apart, and then covered. Tubers may be harvested in nine months but are usually left in the field and dug daily as needed.

Maize is also grown on 95 percent of the farms. Efforts to introduce hybrids have made some progress among foreign colonists, but native peasants prefer traditional varieties, some of which may be primitive. With respect to basic maize types, my limited observations agree essentially with those of the Services.[37] However, among the Mbyá-Guaraní Indians, a small varicolored variety known to them as 90-day maize was encountered, and it is likely that other types are cultivated.[38] Maize is commonly grown in association with other crops, particularly beans and mandioca. Two to five grains per hole are planted, depending upon local preference, with holes and rows spaced approximately 1 yard apart. The crop is harvested when mature, and the ears are hung to dry under the eaves or near the house for convenience in daily use.

Beans are grown on about two thirds of the farms. The botany of Paraguayan beans has not been carefully worked out, and local nomenclature lacks precision. A number of porotos are grown, but the most preferred is known as poroto San Francisco.[39] However, of the several types of porotos, there seem to be local preferences for the other poroto varieties as well. Beans are

TABLE 2

Production of Major Agricultural Commodities, 1942 - 1943

Crop	% of Farms[a]	Total Acreage	No. of Plants[b]
Mandioca	96	140,951	· · ·
Maize	96	243,367	· · ·
Beans	67	51,432	· · ·
Oranges[33]	61	· · ·	4,070,600
Coconuts[34]	51	· · ·	6,768,600
Cotton	50	102,995	· · ·
Bananas[33]	45	· · ·	4,186,500
Peanuts	38	33,988	· · ·
Tangerines[33]	34	· · ·	396,800
Sweet potatoes	32	17,653	· · ·
Sugarcane	23	38,162	· · ·
Tobacco	19	15,153	· · ·
Pineapples	15	· · ·	88,000[c]
Bitter oranges	12	· · ·	19,176,660
Watermelons	11	4,616	· · ·
Peaches	11	· · ·	90,345
Grapes[35]	10	· · ·	407,030
Onions	10	4,800	· · ·
Mangoes[33]	10	· · ·	74,300
Rice	9	20,542	· · ·
Limes	8	· · ·	33,979
Beans[36]	8	4,472	· · ·
Lemons	8	· · ·	27,678
Yerba maté[35]	7	· · ·	2,503,200
Melons	7	1,740	· · ·
Peas	6	3,754	· · ·
Alfalfa	6	4,500	· · ·
Castor beans	3	2,171	· · ·
Grapefruit	2	· · ·	61,930
Wheat[35]	2	6,184	· · ·
Avocados	1.8	· · ·	8,284
Coffee	1.5	· · ·	380,346
Squash	1.4	1,576	· · ·
Potatoes	1.2	1,210	· · ·
Vegetables	0.8	284	· · ·
Sunflowers	0.6	499	· · ·
Broom corn	0.5	762	· · ·
Soybeans	0.5	549	· · ·
Papayas	0.2	· · ·	2,808

Source: Paraguay (1948).

[a]94,498 farms were censused. Figures above 2% rounded to nearest whole percent.

[b]Producing-age.

[c]Estimate.

cultivated both alone and in association with maize. I personally observed beans left to dry in the fields and picked in small quantities for household or market.[40] Farmers shell dried pods by pounding them with a stick on a hide or on a tile floor. They separate hulls by winnowing, using the hands or a small, shallow, circular basket.

Peanuts and sweet potatoes are grown by a significant number of the native farmers, as are pineapples. Members of the cucurbit family are relatively unimportant. Gourds of several varieties are grown sporadically for use as containers, and a squash (zapallo) is found chiefly in the extreme southeastern part of the country.

Cotton, the most important native nonfood crop, is produced on at least half the farms. Introduced varieties are prevalent, although the Services noted several possibly native strains in Tobatí.[41] The cultivation practices described by the Services agree with my own observations. According to the Services, tobacco is the only native field crop that is first planted in viveros (seedbeds). However, the practice is not universal (Figure 21).

FIGURE 21

Tobacco planted in forest clearing, almost indistinguishable from forest litter, second growth, and weeds (La Colmena).

Harvested leaves are bundled and hung in the sun to dry (Figure 22). When sufficiently cured, they are rolled into crude cigars or twisted into a rope about three quarters of an inch thick.

With a few exceptions, introduced plants are unimportant in peasant agriculture. Both wheat and rice were introduced in the Colonial period and have assumed a secondary role in the native diet, but they are grown with indifferent success and must be imported. Wheat in particular is poorly suited to Paraguay and is cultivated primarily by Polish and Ukranian colonists who persist in their attachment to the crop. Rice is grown by Japanese colonists using paddy methods, but elsewhere it is produced on naturally irrigated campo lands as a large-scale commercial enterprise. Among the vegetables only onions are common on native farms. Potatoes, peas, soybeans, and leafy vegetables are grown, but peasants participate little in their production or commerce.

Introduced plants generally adopted in native agriculture include sugarcane and a wide variety of fruits. Sugarcane is found on almost one fourth of the farms. Heaviest production is in the central region within easy reach of the processing plants located near Asunción. Most sugar is processed for alcohol and caña.

FIGURE 22

Tobacco harvested from field, sun-cured on wire supports in front of farmer's dwelling.

In the interior, however, cane is fed to oxen when they perform heavy labor and is squeezed in primitive mills to provide the juice for a popular refreshing drink. The refining of sugar into rapadura (brownish cakes) is a common household industry only in the vicinity of Encarnación, where production was introduced, and it is still controlled by Germans from Brazil.

Fruits, including various citrus fruits, and the banana, mango, and grape, are extremely popular. They are grown commercially, but most peasants plant several varieties of fruit trees and vines close to their dwellings. Citrus fruits are ubiquitous and are consumed in large quantities during the eight months or so that they are available. Avocados and papayas are also grown, but their sensitivity to frost limits their distribution.

In addition to cultivated plants there are a number of more or less wild plants that because of their utility are tolerated and even encouraged in chacras. The native mbocayá palm produces a small "coconut," which is eaten, or pressed for oil, and the tree itself provides fiber, fodder, and building materials. Gathering of the seeds is an important secondary source of income near Asunción, but I could find no instance in which the tree was consciously planted.[42] The fruit of the guava is highly prized. The low shrubs are seldom planted because they grow profusely in upland campos and pastures where the seeds have been randomly scattered by man and beast. The "wild" apepú (bitter orange) is grown commercially for the extraction of petitgrain oil from the leaves, but although primitive stills are occasionally encountered through the countryside, this is not a common peasant pursuit. The tree is often spared in clearing and allowed to propagate naturally in open fields, particularly if the fields are intended as pasture. Sweeter varieties of the apepú are planted for shade, decoration, or juice, but in general it is regarded as part of the natural rather than the cultivated flora. Yerba maté was formerly gathered wild; but although it has been thoroughly incorporated into Paraguayan agriculture, its cultivation is monopolized by foreign colonists.

Cultivation Practices

Paraguayan agricultural technology has failed to mature much beyond early Colonial forms, remaining for the most part exceedingly primitive. To native shifting-cultivators the Spaniards introduced some new crops and a few relatively sophisticated tools and concepts. But although these 16th- and 17th-century improvements became basic to Paraguayan farming, some non-Spanish crops and practices survive. Slash-and-burn cultivation continues to characterize farming in isolated areas, and even in the central region, where field patterns are relatively stable, the shifting tendency is preserved in the practice of bush fallow.

The tool inventory of the average farmer is small, and the components are simple. The machete and a heavy, long-handled hoe are the basic minimum common to all, and perhaps half of the farmers possess no more than these two. The axe is also common. The plow is widespread but by no means universal. The agricultural census counted approximately 64,500 plows of all types but noted that 55 percent of the farms possessed none at all.[43] This deficiency is reduced in part by neighborly lending, but many farmers still carry on cultivation without it. The importance of the plow shows some expectable regional variation. In the central region, where farming is more or less sedentary, farmers are more apt to be equipped with plows than are those in remote areas. However, in Tobatí, only 45 road miles from Asunción, more than three fourths of the farms lack plows.

Approximately 33,200 of the plows are of a primitive, one-handled wooden type (arado yvyrá) that has apparently descended almost unmodified from an early Colonial prototype. Its form suggests that it is related not to the arado dental, which is still found in southern and central Spain and throughout Latin America, but to the arado cuchillo, a type reported from northern Spain (Figure 23).[44] The arado yvyrá is constructed entirely of wood except for a small metal strip affixed to the point of the blade.

Metal moldboard plows of the light "walking" variety (called arado francés by many informants) have been available in Paraguay since the turn of the century, but cost has limited their distribution among the peasants. In addition, although the moldboard plow is more efficient and less awkward than the wooden type, it represents an encumbrance to farmers who are not geographically stabilized by the ownership of land. The arado yvyrá, on the other hand, is easily manufactured and readily abandoned. Attachment to the wooden plow is strengthened by the belief that it is "best for the soil" (which it disturbs very little) and that it is "better" for combating certain weeds.

Other agricultural implements common to Spanish farming in

FIGURE 23

Paraguayan arado yvyrá (wooden plow) near Ybytymí.

the early Colonial period may have been introduced to Paraguay, but their use has not become general. Because cultivation of small grains remained unimportant, many specialized tools did not enter the complex. However, even the more generalized rakes and cultivators failed to become widely adopted.[45]

The principal conveyance is the carreta, a large two-wheeled oxcart with wooden sides and often a protective hood of hides or sheet metal. In 1943, however, there were only 27,000 carretas distributed among 94,500 chacras.[46] In northern Paraguay carretas are large, with spoked, iron-rimmed wheels 6 feet or greater in diameter, and requiring four or more oxen. In the central and southern region, smaller carretas require only two oxen. The alza prima, a specialized two-wheeled conveyance, is used for carrying logs.

Oxen are always yoked in juntas (pairs) whether pulling a carreta or a plow. In Paraguay the horn yoke is universal. The notched shoulder yoke, another common Iberian type, appears in the vicinity of Encarnación where it may have been introduced by German colonists from Brazil. Shoulder yokes also are occasionally used with the alza prima.

Agricultural labor is performed on a family basis. Men normally clear and prepare the soil, and women and children aid in planting, weeding, and harvesting. However, there does not seem to be a strict division of labor. Women left alone by death or abandonment usually seek livelihoods outside the chacra, but some continue to farm, and in areas experiencing prolonged economic distress women continue cultivation while their men seek employment elsewhere. Minga (labor exchange) by neighbors, and more particularly relatives, is extremely common. No responsible neighbor turns down a legitimate request for help, and the only expected return is a similar willingness to respond. Prolonged visits by relatives are frequent. The host is expected to provide bed and board; relatives usually bring food and presents, and help with agricultural tasks. Relatives living close to each other cooperate in farming, sometimes to the extent that individual ownership of the crop and even of the land begins to grow indistinct.

The actual techniques of cultivation are rudimentary. Seasonal change is not precisely marked in the generally mild climate, and the agricultural calendar is correspondingly ill defined. Farmers have established planting and harvesting periods for most crops, but these are long and informal. In local lore, the deciduous lapacho tree, which blooms profusely in August or September, presumably marks the end of killing frosts, but the unreliability of the lapacho is widely recognized. Without seasonal imperatives there is little or no need to mobilize labor on small peasant chacras. Agricultural crises do occur, for example when cotton must be harvested before impending rains, but in general the peasant sense of timing is not highly refined, and resultant failures are usually interpreted simply as caprices of nature.

The informality attending agricultural tasks pervades the entire complex of farming activity. Most jobs are undertaken with little exactitude or relish. Clearing is accomplished with the axe and the machete. As a woodsman, the Paraguayan considers himself second to none; he is contemptuous of colonists' efforts to clear land, and Bunyanesque folk tales center around prowess with an axe. However, there seems to be no such focus of interest upon the mechanics of cultivation.

After clearing, the debris must be burned repeatedly for several years. Large trunks and stumps are left in the field to rot, and stumps often resprout to compete with plantings. In newly cleared land, the hoe is used for what little preparation the soil receives. Where plowing is practiced, the land is occasionally plowed several times at right angles to "break the soil" before opening furrows. Planting is done with a hoe or digging stick or, where plows are employed, seeds or pieces of the plant are simply dropped into the furrows at proper intervals.[47] After plants have been seeded, the foot is used to cover them. Once planted, a field receives little care before harvest. Plants with long growing-seasons, like mandioca, may be weeded more than once, but weeding is generally infrequent.

The concept of fertilization may be vaguely understood, but I could find no evidence of its practice among peasants. Crop rotation is employed, although its conscious relation to conservation is debatable. As the Services note, plants (and foods) are considered "hot" or "cold," and their "temperature" governs their association in fields or their place in rotation. Personal observations indicate that crop rotation is not nearly so systematized as the Services suggest. Most farmers know which crops place the greatest demands upon the soil and would not waste virgin land on mandioca, which will yield sufficiently on depleted soils. Many farmers also admit that continual planting of the same crop is not good for the soil. However, the specific sequence of rotation apparently does not depend upon any traditional formula.

Irrigation for most agricultural plants is normally unnecessary. Even during periodic droughts, however, surplus water is not added to peasant plantings; steep slopes are avoided, but when they are cultivated, rows are planted down slope, and no effort is made to impede erosion.

Like many facets of Paraguayan life, farming is attended by considerable supersitition, and a wide variety of folk beliefs are employed to bridge the gap between practical knowledge and the realm of causation. Agricultural folk superstitions are less significant than formerly, but they are still taken seriously by many farmers. Some lore undoubtedly stems from crude observations of natural phenomena, but much of it is highly mystical. Origins of specific beliefs are not easily traced. Many are heavily infused with Christian elements, and in other ways strongly suggest European influences, but far more investigation is needed before the relative contributions of various ethnic groups can be determined.

Data regarding nature lore are difficult to acquire and are often highly contradictory. Below are listed a few beliefs concerning weather and cultivation that were validated by more than one informant and seem to be part of the cultural equipment of the general farming population.[48]

1. WEATHER   Most weather lore concerns rainfall. If winter rains do not begin by el día de San Juan (June 24), the statue of San Juan is turned to the wall until rains come. Crashing branches in the forest indicate rain, which can be encouraged by taking the olla to the creek or spring and washing it; a cross will also serve, and the act is usually accompanied by prayers. Beating a horse's skull will also produce rain. Tormentas (damaging winds) can be diverted from one's house by cleaving the ground with a hatchet or turning over the log mortar. Walking around the house three times while praying or blessing the wind with cross or rosary is also thought to afford protection.

2. AGRICULTURE   Beliefs connected directly with farming are many and complex. The general feeling seems to be that cultivation must be approached in the proper "spirit." Young plants, like children, are sensitive to individual feelings; hence, if one is ill, jealous, vengeful, and so on, he should not enter the chacra, or his bad spirit will be transmitted to his plants. Crops are "prejudiced" by having a passerby stop and admire them, or by having them exposed to teterasú.[49] To guard against such phenomena, a horse's skull is placed on a stick overlooking the field to divert the words or the gaze of those intending or inadvertently bearing ill. A good harvest is assured by placing broken maize cobs or a small pile of peanut shells in the road "cross" nearest the field at planting time. Tobacco should not be harvested when the south wind is blowing, or the leaves will fall apart. Changes in the weather are particularly dangerous because they represent changes in the whole complex of Nature; hence, if you are planting and the naturaleza changes, work must be abandoned.

The moon is central to agricultural folklore and affects the cutting of wood and thatch as well. Most plants, including maize, peanuts, and beans, must be sown during the waning moon, or they will be full of worms. Mandioca, on the other hand, must be planted during the waxing moon, or it will be fibrous, thick-skinned, and inedible.

Livestock may be cured of various ills by individuals thought to be particularly gifted in such matters. Cures take many forms, depending upon the ailment and the modus operandi of the curer, and the most powerful healers do not even need to see the animal. Such individuals are most often called upon to remove fly larva from beneath the hide of the host; uras supposedly drop off the animal within 24 hours of "treatment."

Livestock

The raising of livestock is a basic feature of Paraguayan land use. Most cattle and sheep are to be found on large estancias that are engaged in commercial production, and since such enterprises require considerable land and capital, peasants are excluded except as laborers. However, ranching has profoundly affected patterns of rural living. By the late 18th century, the complex of traits usually identified with gauchismo was widespread in the Plata region and firmly established in Paraguay where ranching was the preferred occupation.[50] Most of the grazing land in eastern Paraguay was pre-empted early in the Colonial period, but the bulk of the population, although forced to farm for a livelihood, assumed many cultural elements more appropriate to the estancia than to the chacra.

Meat, almost entirely in the form of beef, is a mainstay of the Paraguayan diet:

> According to national statistics, about 65,000,000 kilos of meat, mainly beef, are consumed locally each year. This amounts to about 180 grams of meat per person per day . . . . Meat is the symbolic staff of life to a Paraguayan. . . . People feel they are suffering if they have none.[51]

Meat is consumed in many forms, including charque (jerked beef) and asado (the outdoor barbecue).

Traditional patterns of male dress also reflect ranching influences. Older styles are fast giving way to simplified western clothing, but baggy bombachas are still worn in rural districts, and the faja (the wide woven waistband) is still customary. The chiripá (fringed leather apron) is occasionally found, but other elements typical of the equestrian costume have disappeared or were never adopted. Berets or simple straw hats are worn, and footwear—of any kind—is not widely used.

Rural Paraguayans have also preserved a strong predilection

for horses and horsemanship. Horses are rarely employed in
farm work, yet nearly 60 percent of the farms reported owning
horses in 1942-1943, and in the country as a whole they substan-
tially outnumbered oxen.[52] Equestrian trappings and skills are
greatly admired, and racing and other forms of riding competition
are important in rural social and recreational activity. Mules
and burros are numerous, but they are considered inferior creatures.

Although few Paraguayans specialize in livestock ranching,
almost all who farm also care for a few animals or poultry (see
Table 3). Small farm animals are particularly common; sheep
and goats are not numerous, but chickens are ubiquitous,[53] and
pigs are kept on more than two thirds of the chacras. Large farm
animals are also surprisingly numerous. Dairy cattle are kept
on more than half the farms; milk is consumed fresh, and the
surplus, if any, is made into a bland white cheese.[54] Other cattle
(presumably oxen) are reported on 58 percent of the farms.

Care given to farm animals depends greatly upon their function.
Care of horses is lavish in comparison with that given to other

TABLE 3

Livestock on Paraguayan Farms, 1942 - 1943

Animal	No. of Farms[a]	No. of Units
Fowl[b]	87,553	2,605,396
Pigs	63,959	227,326
Cattle[c]	54,878	503,360
Horses	54,361	180,438
Milk cows	51,194	177,509
Oxen	35,040	120,134
Sheep	7,434	108,865
Burros[d]	7,002	10,349
Goats	1,697	11,478
Mules	1,521	2,669

Source: Paraguay (1948), pp. 192-205.

[a]94,498 farms were censused.

[b]Aves de corral—includes all barnyard fowl, but chickens are the only
significant ones.

[c]Other than milk cows and oxen.

[d]From personal observations, proportion of burros to other farm animals appears far greater than the statistics indicate.

animals; when possible they are provided with supplementary feed and protection in inclement weather. Dairy cattle and oxen receive maize and sugarcane when producing or working. Mandioca is fed to animals, and fodder—usually palm leaves—is also cut. Alfalfa is not commonly grown, but forage grasses are often planted in yards and in small piquetes (fenced pastures) near dwellings. However, native grasses are the basic diet of all herbivores, and pigs and barnyard fowl are fed kitchen refuse or left to their own devices. Animals are seldom confined or sheltered. Pigs and milk cows may be tied by one leg to a convenient tree, but animals and fowl are usually allowed to roam unfettered.

The Rural Economy

The Paraguayan peasant is often described as a subsistence farmer. Detailed studies are lacking, but evidence suggests that if "subsistence" implies complete dependence upon only what can be individually produced, the term is not applicable. Farmers plant to meet their own food needs, and these tasks usually have highest priority. However, in the central region, farmers commonly devote half or more of their land to crops intended for sale. In isolated regions self-sufficiency is approached, but even here farmers are dependent to some degree upon processed or manufactured goods, and must earn capital or exchange to acquire them.[55]

Sources of income are varied in the campaña, but most capital is earned by production of farm surpluses or by wage labor outside the farm. The conscious production of marketable surpluses and purely commercial crops has long been practiced. Cotton and tobacco are traditional in peasant agriculture, and home industries consume only a small percentage of the production. In 1943, cotton was grown on half of all Paraguayan farms, and one fifth of the farms grew tobacco.[56] Farms producing commercial nonfood crops tend to concentrate in areas readily accessible to markets. In the central zone, 86 percent of the chacras produce cotton. However, in remote parts of the country, cotton and tobacco are also common crops.

Staple foods are often sown in amounts sufficient to assure a small surplus. Maize, beans, peanuts, sugarcane, fruit such as melons, and onions all have market possibilities, and mandioca, particularly when converted into almidón (starch) is also potentially profitable. The degree to which major crops are commercialized is summarized in Table 4.

Among landless peasants, wage labor must often be substituted for commercial agriculture. Employment opportunities exist in extractive industries and the growing urban centers, but the principal demand remains in agriculture. Foreign colonies are particularly important in this regard, because most pioneers practice commercial agriculture on a scale that requires additional seasonal labor. Statistics indicate that the operators of approximately half the Paraguayan farms seek employment elsewhere and spend an average of 76 days per year working for others.[57]

Some Paraguayans manage occasionally to supplement farm income by hunting, gathering, home manufacture, or performing services. Near cities, the mbocayá nut is collected and sold to processing plants, and bitter-orange leaves, wild yerba, and hides of various animals are marketable. Near towns or along major transportation routes women bake chipa (bread from mandioca flour) for sale at fiestas, cantinas, or to transients. The weaving of rope and lassos and the making of hats, fans, pottery, and knives are "cottage industries" that occasionally develop into specializations but are used primarily to supplement farm income.

The mechanics of exchange are undergoing change in rural Paraguay. Older informants report nostalgically that the money economy was formerly unimportant. Neighbors freely exchanged labor and yopoí (produce). In neither case was exchange formalized in terms of standard values; surpluses were simply distributed

TABLE 4

Off-Farm Sale of Major Agricultural Commodities, 1942 - 1943

Crop	Farms Producing	Farms Selling
Mandioca	90,576	14,692
Maize	90,265	32,455
Beans	62,865	18,522
Cotton	47,579	46,331
Peanuts	36,079	11,769
Sweet potatoes	30,164	4,075
Sugarcane	21,912	7,090
Tobacco	18,104	13,976

Source: Paraguay (1948), pp. 131-156.

when available, and neighbors were expected to do likewise. A few rows of cotton or tobacco were planted for barter to itinerant peddlers for caña, yerba maté, clothing, utensils, and trinkets; medical, magic, or religious services were paid for with livestock, agricultural produce, or reciprocal favors.

In remote parts of Paraguay, sharing and barter are still prevalent, but as serviceable roads have penetrated into the campaña, rural towns have become important collecting centers for agricultural produce, and more and more peasants have been drawn into the complex web of commercial interdependence. Peasants living near major roads now transport farm surpluses directly to Asunción by mixtos (trucks).[58] However, most produce is brought by oxcart to towns where it is sold to revendedores (middlemen). Since revendedores are often local merchants, peasants still barter their crops for manufactured goods but in a monetary frame of reference. From small market towns, or boliches in isolated areas, produce trickles into Asunción for distribution, processing, or export.

Both collection and production are poorly organized. Revendedores usually have specific contacts who contract for all they collect. However, entrepreneurs in the capital receive goods from all over the country, and as there is little contact between regions or between various segments of the economy, there is no guarantee of price or even of a market. The position of the revendedores, who operate on a small margin and are often without adequate storage facilities, is highly speculative.

The basic and least dependable variable is the peasant producer. His agricultural regimen is only loosely fixed, and what he will grow, and in what amounts, depends upon whim, tradition, or his own interpretation of agricultural economics. Unfortunately the intricacies of commercial involvement usually escape him. Furthermore, his sense of future is poorly developed, and credit, market timing, or speculation for improved return are not part of his cultural experience. If seasonal glut robs him of a fair price, he accepts it fatalistically, rationalizing his loss by employment of standard blame-mechanisms.[59]

THE NATIONAL ECONOMY

Within the Paraguayan economic framework are established opportunities and limitations that have profoundly affected both viability and cultural geography of pioneer settlement. To some extent, as noted below, immigrant pioneers have utilized superior technical skills and strong motivations for economic betterment to devise new sources of wealth. But successful new enterprises have seldom departed totally from traditional ones, and both old and new must face realities inherent in the Paraguayan milieu.

In many ways, Paraguay's economy is little more than the aggregate of individual peasant economies. Upon an agrarian base emphasizing family subsistence, a modest commercial enterprise with involvements in foreign markets has been grafted. Some natural resources are available for exploitation, and these, as well as the production of native agriculture, provide the raw materials for a small industrial development. However, historical and geographic factors continue to conspire against economic growth; raw materials still dominate the country's small volume of exports, and Paraguay's foreign trade is concerned primarily with her immediate neighbors.

Resources

The value of Paraguay's natural endowment depends somewhat upon point of view. Paraguayans are generally convinced that their country is a storehouse of minerals, mostly of the precious variety. Although some small iron deposits near Ybycuý were worked of necessity during the War of the Triple Alliance, explorations have yet to uncover any significant deposits of minerals other than limestone and building materials. Furthermore, there is little reason for optimism regarding future discoveries.[60]

Paraguay's extensive forests, on the other hand, represent an unquestioned source of wealth. Timber and quebracho extract usually account for more than one half of the country's exports by value. Since Paraguay lacks mineral fuels or hydroelectric development, forests, in the form of trosa (firewood) or charcoal, must also supply much of the country's inanimate energy. Several subtropical hardwoods have steady markets in the Plata region, and selective logging has long taken place on the accessible margins of Paraguay's forests, particularly on the Paraná Plateau.[61] It is estimated, however, that more than 12 million acres of unexploited forest remain.

Foreign pioneers have been quick to recognize opportunities in forestry. Isolation of colonies from mills and markets has restricted logging, but in some cases the price of land and even the selection of settlement sites have been determined by the presence of merchantable timber.[62] Colonists have occasionally been able to dispose of timber cut in the process of clearing, and in extreme cases, as in the Mennonite settlement of Sommerfeld, lumbering has assumed the dominant role in the colony's economy.

Perhaps the most significant and extensive of Paraguay's resources is potentially productive land. The eastern part of the country contains approximately 61,700 square miles, of which less than 3 percent is actually under cultivation. Almost all the remainder is appropriate for some form of pastoral or agricultural land use.

Pastoral Industries

The raising of cattle, in addition to its traditional role in Paraguayan life, remains a mainstay of commercial exchange. The internal market for meat, animals, and some animal products, is relatively dependable, and hides, meat, and meat products are standard though declining export items.[63] Large foreign companies with immense landholdings have dominated the processing and export phases, but the native rancher with a few thousand acres of campo and several hundred head is still characteristic in the eastern region. Foreign colonists have occasionally turned to stock raising when other enterprises failed, but few pioneers possess the inclination or capital for ranching or dairying.[64] Although many farmers raise animals of some kind, these activities are subordinate to cultivation.

Agriculture

Estimates of the amount of cultivable land in eastern Paraguay vary widely. It is generally assumed that at least 12 million acres remain for agricultural development—sufficient to sustain one million Paraguayan peasant families at current levels of exploitation, or to accommodate perhaps 100,000 immigrant families on parcels of 120 acres. At the moment, the value of such land for foreign colonization is largely hypothetical. Because immigrants have shown little proclivity for operating consistently at the level of the Paraguayan peasant, the utility of the country's surplus land must be considered in the context of commercial cultivation. Yet most available land remains well beyond reach of the national economy.

Problems of commercial agriculturists in Paraguay are connected less with production than with other economic factors. Immigrants usually have technical skills adequate to grow almost anything within the rather wide range of ecological possibilities. The principal difficulty lies in selecting crops that can be marketed profitably. Food staples are in demand in growing urban centers, and wheat, rice, and sugar are grown in insufficient quantities. But the internal market is relatively small, and to supply it colonists must compete with low-cost producers accustomed to small profit-margins. Production for export also presents problems. Agricultural commodities, including cotton, tobacco, maize, oil of petitgrain, and fruit, are regularly shipped abroad. However, poorly developed internal communications greatly hinder the movement of goods, and both distance and isolation place the country's produce at an extraordinary competitive disadvantage.

The Paraguayan road net has expanded slowly during the last decade. Nevertheless, although a few centers of pioneer settlement have attracted serviceable roads, there is still no road connecting the northern part of the country with the capital, and many other areas, including older population centers, are similarly isolated. In 1959 there were still only 100 miles of paved road beyond the limits of Asunción. The all-weather roads noted in Figure 1 (p. 2) total some 700 miles and are technically capable of bearing a continuous flow of vehicular traffic. The government wisely prohibits movement during rains, but even with this precaution such roads are poorly maintained.[65]

Paraguay's only significant railroad, extending 274 miles from Asunción to Encarnación, is one of South America's oldest, and since early in the 20th century it has provided international connections via ferry and the Argentine National Railway at Posadas, Misiones.[66] But the railroad serves a very limited portion of the country, and although managed by a British company, earnings have been insufficient to maintain the line properly. Usefulness of the railroad is further restricted by high freight rates and inefficiency in cargo handling.

Paraguay's fluvial network traditionally has been and continues to be the only feasible means of regular commercial intercourse with other countries. It is important to note that Paraguay's river system has seldom functioned effectively as a commercial lifeline, and location of colonies upon navigable waterways is not so advantageous as might be supposed. In addition to physical limitations dealt with elsewhere,[67] Paraguayan shipping is antiquated, inefficient, expensive, and subject to arbitrary government regulation. The use of the better-equipped Argentine fleet is also arbitrarily circumscribed.

The lack of modern commercial mechanisms in the native economic infrastructure poses additional problems. Producers, whether colonist or native, must develop means of transport, processing, and marketing in order to function. Yet such developments are almost impossible except for corporate or cooperative forms of capital accumulation. The cash yield from individual chacras rarely provides surplus funds for improvements or expansion. Production costs are generally low, but marketing costs are high, and the profit margin of the most efficient producer is small. Furthermore, almost all agricultural paraphernalia, including fertilizer, must be imported at several times their cost in more accessible areas.

In competition for small internal and export markets, political considerations often overshadow other factors, but market possibilities themselves are highly variable. As in other Latin American countries, economic enterprise is characterized by volatile speculative instability. In Paraguay, cyclic fluctuations can hardly be compared in magnitude with those of Brazil, but shortage-induced high prices have led almost invariably to overproduction and collapse.

The odds against rapid accumulation of wealth have prompted many of Paraguay's colonists to abandon cultivation or to leave Paraguay altogether. Japanese pioneers, however, consistently derive profit from traditional Paraguayan staples, and some enterprising colonists have managed to devise new and relatively consistent sources of wealth. Yerba maté, tung, grapes, bitter orange, and coffee were introduced into Paraguayan cultivation by foreigners, and production is still concentrated in pioneer settlements.

The Ilex was brought under cultivation around 1909, and production spread rapidly throughout German settlements.[68] Before 1933 the yerba industry was lucrative. In that year Argentine plantations came into production, and the boom collapsed, but yerba plantations continue to yield a modest income. Within the last 10 years cultivation has entirely replaced gathering from wild varieties, and foreign colonists currently account for about 80 percent of Paraguay's yerba production.

According to informants, tung was brought to the Alto Paraná region in the 1920's by Wilhelm Gessner, a German Swiss. The tree began to assume importance in colonies on the Paraguayan shore about 1935, and war-induced shortages permitted handsome profits from 1939 to 1950. World need has now diminished while supplies have increased, and there is little interest in new plantings.

Viticulture and wine making were initiated by German colonists in Independencia, but success was not immediate, the preferred alcoholic drink being caña, even among urban upper classes. However, the market has been slowly expanding, and those with large acreages in production are now reaping the benefits. Unfortunately the internal market is nearly saturated; export is not feasible and recently expanded plantings will prove far less profitable.

Distillation of petitgrain oil was undertaken in the 1870's by the French botanist Balanza. Paraguay now produces most of the world's supply; as with yerba maté, cultivation has largely displaced gathering from wild trees. However, demand is small and variable, and because Paraguayan petitgrain is inferior in quality, it is easily displaced on world markets.

Coffee has been the subject of numerous experiments in Paraguay dating back to the last century. It is currently grown successfully on higher slopes in the Central Hill Belt, particularly in the German colonies of Altos and Independencia. In 1954 the Compañía Americana de Fomento Económico (CAFE) was organized near Pedro Juan Caballero on the Brazilian border. In preparing "plantations" for sale to absentee investors, some four million coffee trees were planted, but a severe frost in 1957 destroyed the first harvest, and in 1959 the company went bankrupt. Some owners subsequently came to live on their land, but the future of the project is clouded.

Foreign pioneers, in addition to experimenting with new plants, have also attempted in various ways to resolve problems of mar-

keting. The most commonly applied solution has been the formation of agricultural cooperatives. Not all immigrant groups have
a cultural predisposition for cooperative enterprise, and even
among those who do, cooperatives are not always successful.
But where employed, the cooperatives have generally enhanced
the economic climate of the entire colony. By combining productive resources, colonists have acquired transport and processing
facilities, developed greater control over price and market, and
in rare instances been able to circumvent internal economic or
political forces.

THE SOCIO-POLITICAL MILIEU

The purview of geographers does not normally encompass elements of nonmaterial culture. Yet in the study of pioneer settlement, in which immigrants face exposure to an alien culture as
well as an alien environment, the artificial isolation of man - land
relationships from their total behavioral context is all but impossible. Paraguayan values, mores, and political organization have
most certainly influenced the reactions of foreigners to their new
situations and have thus contributed to both form and function in
the cultural landscape of pioneer settlement.

It is difficult to generalize about the impact of the Paraguayan
personality upon foreign colonists because several highly contrasting cultures have been involved in pioneer settlement. Obviously
Mediterranean Europeans find a few familiar cues, and Spaniards
in particular tend to view Paraguayans as a benighted but more
or less recognizable extension of themselves. Northern Europeans
and Asiatics, on the other hand, have encountered cultural contrasts that in many ways have proved exceedingly difficult to rec-
oncile.

The nature of peasant life-goals and acceptable means of attain-
ing them have been a particularly common source of conflict for
foreigners. The "psychological immobility" usually ascribed to
Latin Americans is well developed in Paraguay. Few peasants
plan their activities very far in advance. Speculation about the
future is considered fruitless, and contingencies must be met
with available resources. Labor occupies a relatively low position
in the scale of values; it is undertaken to meet elemental needs,

and even these do not always exert the necessary pressure. Subsistence accomplished without steady employment is not frowned upon, and luck rather than effort is considered the key to success.

Closely related to these cultural characteristics is the trait of macho and its corollary, vivo. These concepts are difficult to define,[69] but in Paraguay they produce undisciplined behavior that contrasts decidedly with northern-European and Oriental moral and ethical codes. Male virility must constantly be verified by acts of sexual conquest, physical prowess, or feats of bravery. Such conduct often runs counter to established legal restrictions or social conventions, but is almost openly admired if accomplished with a flare of derring-do that captures local imagination.

Paraguayan family organization serves to intensify the cultural contrasts between peasants and foreigners. In rural Paraguay, many family unions lack civil or religious sanction. The strength of such attachments is often equal to that of more formalized relationships. However, male feelings of responsibility, even toward children resulting from "free unions," is not always equivalent to foreign notions of family integrity. Even in formalized relationships there is no premium on fidelity, and illegitimacy remains high. Accountably, foreigners tend to resist intermarriage of their female progeny in the fear that these women will ultimately be abandoned.

Of particular significance to the present work are elements of Paraguayan culture that condition response to foreign contact. Attempts to gather information on this matter proved difficult, and the data acquired are insufficient to support more than highly tentative conclusions. Isolation and a unique set of historical circumstances have conspired to limit severely the exposure of Paraguayans to outside influences. Not unexpectedly, geographic and historic introversion have produced a strong ethnocentrism. Paraguay's role in the settlement of the Plata region and in two major wars has helped to develop a deep sense of national consciousness, and exaltation of Guaraní heritage, particularly the language, has given a cultural base to nationalism.

In the crystallization of Paraguayan culture few mechanisms have evolved to accommodate the experience of foreign contact. The specific consequences of this lack of experience, as well as the tenacious adherence to proved values, are not easily traced. The suspicion surrounding foreigners in the period of transition from colony to "republic" was greatly magnified by subsequent dictators, and is still evident in some ways. When foreigners began to arrive in some numbers late in the 19th century, their superior technical and material achievements were regarded with a mixture of awe and embarrassment. But the Paraguayan sense of inferiority was at least superficially obscured as foreigners rapidly demonstrated their lack of capacity in routine but valued patterns of behavior. Inability to master use of the axe and the horse, or to function as Paraguaynas do in their own environment, seems to have reinforced feelings of ethnic security and to have solidified basic attitudes against forces of potential change.

As a consequence of cultural inflexibility, Paraguayans responsible for immigration and colonization have been inclined to perceive the needs of foreign pioneers only in terms of their own peasants. The simple provision of potentially productive land has been thought adequate, and peasants themselves find it difficult to understand why foreigners cannot be satisfied with a commodity that few peasants could aspire to possess. Paraguayans have similarly failed to comprehend foreign dissatisfaction with the typical agrarian-livelihood pattern as a life goal. Alien attitudes toward continual economic advance and wealth accumulation produce negative reactions in the form of feelings of exploitation and resentment of the advantages granted to immigrants as inducements to settle in Paraguay.

Foreigners have discovered also that Paraguayan society is highly resistant to penetration. It may be argued with some conviction that few immigrants have viewed assimilation as advantageous or desirable. Nevertheless, the barriers to acceptance appear formidable. It is not unusual to find second and even third generations of immigrant families referred to as gringos. In Paraguay this term is not the automatically contemptuous epithet that it is in some other Latin American countries; it simply refers, among other things, to an outsider who does not, and cannot, completely share indigenous traditions. Neither intermarriage nor acquisition of the Guaraní language seems to temper the reserve that characterizes Paraguayans in their relationships with outsiders.

An important corollary is the common failure to apply indigenous social restrictions to foreigners. Such a generalization must be regarded with due caution, but in zones of concentrated pioneer settlement it is observable that, in dealings with foreigners, Paraguayans do not necessarily feel bound by social strictures that ordinarily circumscribe their behavior. In fact, instances can be found in which conscious exploitation of pioneers,

mostly in petty ways, is taken as a matter of course, as indicated
by one informant who felt foreign colonies were simply another
natural resource. Obviously the temptation to exploit such a resource is almost irresistible, and to the successful, there is the
dividend of appearing macho or vivo.

Paraguay's political patterns are an additional source of friction. Governmental activities have been largely detrimental to
the progress of pioneer settlement in a variety of ways. Specific
problems accrue from mismanaged efforts to regulate prices,
production, tariffs, and taxes. But failure to provide roads,
schools, credit, or otherwise attend to the interests of the colonists is a more common basis for complaint.

The system of colony administration has also provided considerable grounds for conflict. In colonies, government authority is
vested in native administrators—petty officials appointed on the
basis of political fealty rather than capability, whose authority
is nearly absolute. In the past this authority has been grossly
abused, and results of appeals to higher legal mechanisms have
not necessarily corresponded to the foreigner's sense of justice.

Superimposed upon the relationships between the State and
its colonies is the broader problem of continual political instability. The progression of revolutions has not only tended to discour-
age immigration and to prevent formulation of a coherent, long-
range colonization policy, but also has created an atmosphere of
insecurity similar to that which many colonists had experienced
in their home country and sought to avoid by emigration. Paraguayan revolutions seldom involve prolonged or widespread armed
conflict. However, during the frequent times of political stress
the country's borders are sealed, communications and commerce
within the country are brought to a virtual halt, and the loss of
property and even of lives is an ever-present possibility.

The net effects of government inefficiency, corruption, and
instability have been to compound the difficulties in adjustment
experienced by immigrants. The constant threat to person and
belongings, while often exaggerated, has caused a few colonists
to leave Paraguay and is responsible for widespread discontent
and lack of initiative among those who have remained.

CHAPTER 3

La Colmena-An Example of Cultural Landscape in Japanese Colonies

JAPANESE settlement in Paraguay has been neither extensive nor continuous.[1] Until well into the present century, Paraguay was reluctant to admit Orientals, and the Japanese themselves preferred pioneering in countries with greater reputations for opportunity. Then in 1934 Brazil, the principal recipient of Japanese emigration to South America, set strict quotas on Oriental immigration, and Japan was forced to seek other outlets for her surplus population.[2]

In 1936 Paraguay agreed to accept approximately 100 families on a trial basis, and these settlers established the colony of La Colmena, 81 miles southeast of Asunción. World War II interrupted immigration until 1955. In that year a private company, organized to promote Japanese colonization in Paraguay, brought 137 families to Colonia Presidente Chávez near Encarnación.[3] Two years later a Japanese colonization company established several hundred families in Colonia Fram, also near Encarnación.[4]

By May of 1958, 736 families consisting of 4,660 individuals had entered Paraguay.[5] From the pattern of distribution of Japanese (Figure 24), it is apparent that most of them have remained in the original colony sites. The marked concentration in northeastern Paraguay involves contract laborers of

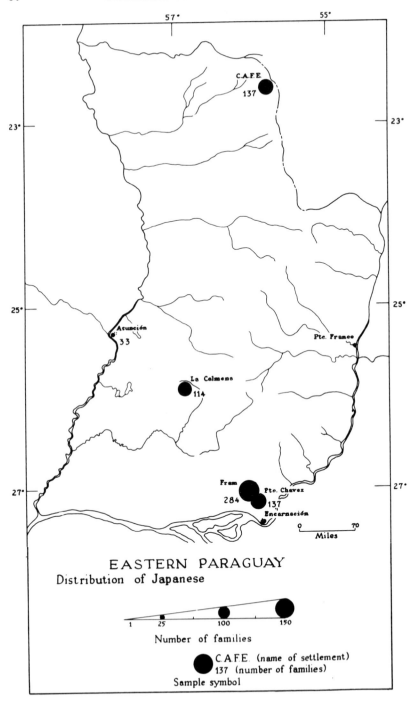

EASTERN PARAGUAY
Distribution of Japanese

Number of families

C.A.F.E. (name of settlement)
137 (number of families)
Sample symbol

FIGURE 24

Compañía Americana de Fomento Económico (CAFE), few of
whom have chosen to settle permanently in Paraguay.

In the Paraguayan milieu Japanese colonists have encountered
extraordinary contrasts with accustomed patterns, and the landscape within their settlements reflects a variety of observable
compromises in traditional behavior. Examination and analysis
of these compromises, as well as those elements of man - land
association that have remained distinctly Japanese, are undertaken in the form of a case study of La Colmena. As the first
Japanese settlement founded in the country, La Colmena is the
only one in which sufficient time has elapsed to permit the
crystallization of cultural change into observable landscape
features. In addition, later colonies have been located in the
zone of greatest concentration of foreign pioneer settlement, and
interaction between Oriental colonists and the Paraguayan milieu
has been obscured by close association with other pioneer ethnic
groups. Later arrivals are also buffered against the effects of
their new circumstances by adequate capitalization, by a high
degree of internal organization, and by the prospect of uninter-
rupted contact with their homeland.

SITE AND SITUATION

Unlike many pioneer groups in South America, the Japanese have
usually based the selection of settlement sites upon careful investigation of alternatives. Almost immediately after promulga-
tion of the order permitting Japanese to enter Paraguay,[6] a
small team of Japanese agronomic experts began to survey the
eastern portion of the country for suitable land. However, the
actual choice of site was conditioned by the location of land
available for purchase and by arbitrary limits placed upon the
survey team by the company responsible for Japanese settlement
abroad.[7]

The site ultimately selected was a 24,000-acre plot known
as Consesión Iriarte, at the northern foot of the Cerro Apitaguá,
an isolated, linear, east-west trending ridge of volcanic origin
(Figure 25).[8] Through most of its 25-mile length, the Cerro
Apitaguá ascends abruptly to an altitude of 2,000 feet above sea
level from relatively level campo lands. On the north, however,

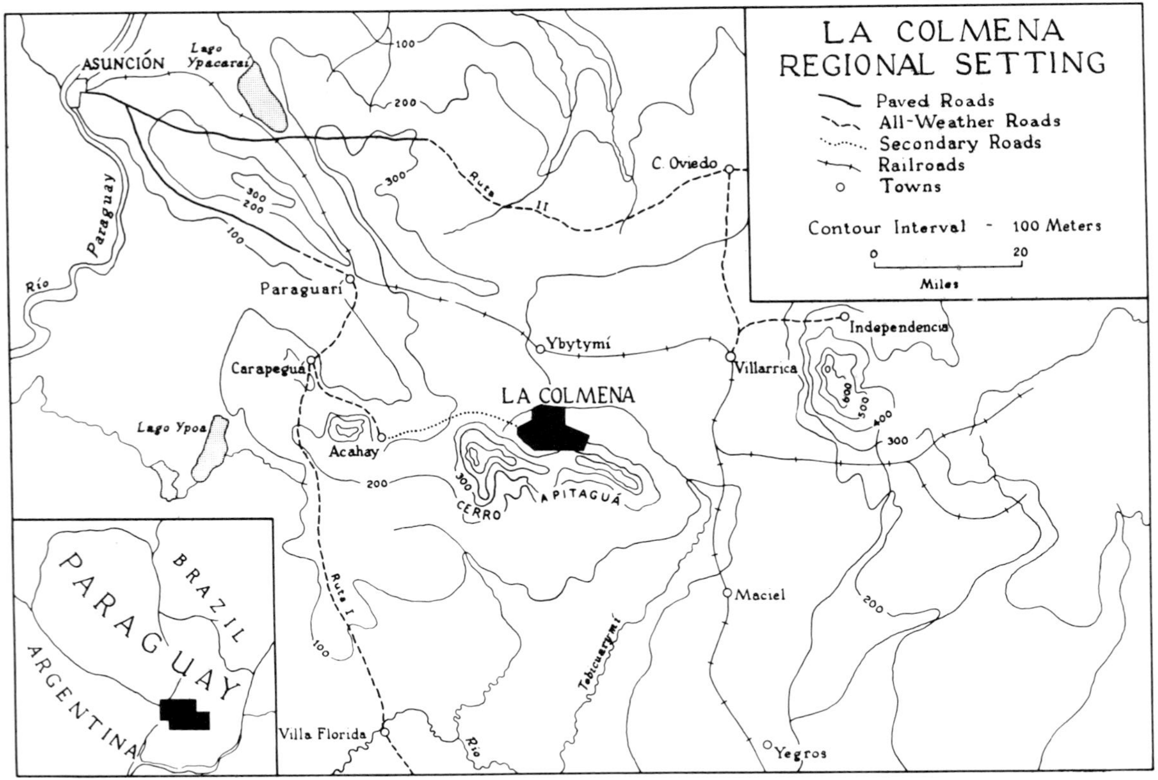
LA COLMENA
REGIONAL SETTING
Paved Roads
All-Weather Roads
Secondary Roads
Railroads
Towns
Contour Interval - 100 Meters
0
20
Miles
ASUNCIÓN
Lago Ypacaraí
Río Paraguay
Paraguarí
Carapeguá
Lago Ypoa
Acahay
Ruta II
Ruta I
C. Oviedo
Ybytymí
Villarrica
Independencia
LA COLMENA
CERRO
APITAGUÁ
Maciel
Yegros
Villa Florida
Río
Tebicuarymí
PARAGUAY
BRAZIL
ARGENTINA

FIGURE 25

the central and eastern flanks incline gently upward to a height of approximately 1,000 feet before resuming their steep ascent to the summit.

It is principally upon these gently sloping lands, elevated from 100 to 400 feet above the surrounding lowlands, that La Colmena is located. This upland has been dissected into broad, roughly parallel interfluves that extend northward some 5.5 miles from the Cerro Apitaguá. The gentle slope of interfluve surfaces, which vary in width from half a mile to two miles or more, is obscured by broad swells and shallow, poorly drained depressions. Interfluves are separated by abrupt declivities formed by permanent streams that are incised 10 to 40 feet below the general level of the surface. Through most of the year these streams occupy only the bottoms of their narrow, steep-sided courses, but water level is subject to considerable fluctuations. Along several of the streams, particularly the Arroyo Tranquara, small, discontinuous, poorly drained terraces are elevated slightly above the bed.

From 1938 to 1945 a weather station was maintained in La Colmena, and monthly averages for various meteorological phenomena are listed in Table 5. Although the climate appears to be somewhat more moist than that of Asunción,[9] La Colmena shares with the rest of the country the problems of extreme rainfall variability. Droughts were recorded in 1941, 1942, and 1947, and in several years untimely rains prevented harvesting of cotton. Temperature contrasts with Asunción are more difficult to assess. The slightly higher elevation of colony lands is thought to moderate summer extremes. Frosts are rare but possible in any month from May to September, and the incidence is apparently slightly greater than in the agricultural zone near the capital.

Soils mantling most of the colony lands are primarily deep, red, friable sandy loams without pronounced profiles. In wells and road cuts these soils show little or no observable changes for depths of more than 30 feet and often possess a remarkable quasi-loessal quality in their ability to stand in vertical walls. Fertility is comparable to that of other well-drained forest soils. However, because of their sandy texture, the original survey team questioned the soils' ability to withstand prolonged cultivation. In fact, agricultural productivity has steadily declined, and among some farmers yields are less than one half those realized during the first few years after clearing.

TABLE 5

Temperature and Rainfall, La Colmena

Month	Temperature[a]		Humidity (%)	Rainfall (in.)[c]
	Average Maximum (°F)[b]	Average Minimum (°F)[b]		
January	100.0	51.8	76.0	4.8
February	100.0	51.8	84.4	4.3
March	95.0	55.4	80.6	6.5
April	91.4	41.0	84.4	7.7
May	89.6	33.8	87.0	6.7
June	86.0	39.2	87.3	5.1
July	87.8	35.6	83.8	2.8
August	93.2	35.6	81.0	2.9
September	93.2	33.8	81.6	3.0
October	97.8	42.8	82.6	5.8
November	95.0	50.0	78.0	8.6
December	102.2	51.8	70.6	5.7

Source: Fujio Moriya, General Manager, Cooperativa La Colmena, SRL.

[a]Average annual temperature, 73°F.
[b]Temperatures converted from degrees centigrade.
[c]Average annual precipitation, 63.9 in.

Vegetation in the vicinity of La Colmena includes representatives of three of Paraguay's principal associations. Well-drained interfluves support dense growths of subtropical semi-deciduous forest; trees are closely spaced and form a complete canopy 50 to 70 feet above the ground, with some trees reaching heights of 100 feet or more. Some typical Alto Paraná forest components are lacking entirely (Ilex) or are restricted in their distribution (bamboos), but most of the common arboreal species are represented, including the wild bitter orange. In preparing the land for agriculture, large blocks of forest have been removed, particularly along the colony's principal roads, although an estimated 50 percent of the original cover remains.

Since the colonizing company insisted that most of the site be forested, there is little grassland within the colony. Lowland campo occurs along the northwestern boundary and in isolated patches along the Tebicuary-mí. A small area of upland campo existed at the present site of the town of La Colmena.

The situational attributes of La Colmena were carefully considered by the survey team. The colonization company, apparently in recognition of the relation between isolation and failure of pioneer enterprises, restricted the possibilities to an area within 100 miles of the capital and stressed locations within easy reach of functioning transportation routes.

In spite of such precautions, the site chosen has proved less than ideal. La Colmena lies well within the prescribed distance from the capital (approximately 65 air miles) and is relatively close to the outer fringe of Paraguay's densely settled core. The problem of accessibility was considered solved by establishment of the colony 16 miles south of Ybytymí, a station 68 miles from the Paraguayan capital on the Asunción-Buenos Aires Railroad. Unfortunately, serviceable connecting roads were entirely lacking. Colonists labored for more than four years to extend a road to Ybytymí, only to discover that, for reasons discussed earlier, rail connections offered little advantage to the settlement. In 1946 a road was built 20 miles westward to the town of Acahay in order to connect the colony with the network of roads radiating from the capital. Upon completion of the road, the truck rapidly became the only significant instrument of colony commerce, and the road to Ybytymí was abandoned.

The shift in emphasis from rail to truck has as yet only slightly improved communication. From Asunción to Carapeguá (44 miles) the route coincides with Ruta I, an all-weather road, 31 miles of which are asphalt surfaced. The 17 miles of secondary road from Carapeguá to Acahay are passable except during prolonged or heavy rains. Beyond Acahay the road is difficult to traverse in any weather; a truck journey without incident requires 7.5 hours to negotiate the 81 miles from the colony to the capital, but during rainy weather communication beyond colony borders is totally suspended, and after each rainstorm as much as a week may be required before campo lands drain sufficiently to permit the passage of motor vehicles. Today the colony cooperative owns a truck that makes more or less regular trips to Asunción, and several individuals own or have access to trucks, which serve to unite the colony with the rest of the country. In 1958, one owner converted his truck to a mixto, which makes two round trips weekly depending upon the weather and the condition of the vehicle. A small area of unimproved campo near the town of La Colmena has been designated an airfield. It is suitable for light planes during dry weather but is little utilized.

DEVELOPMENT OF THE COLONY

In May, 1936, a small group of Japanese were sent to the site of the new colony to survey the land and to lay out roads and property boundaries. The few Paraguayan families scattered as squatters in the colony were given the option of purchasing lots, and several chose to remain.

In establishing their settlement the Japanese did not alter local toponymy. The Paraguayan proclivity for identifying minute landscape details through their outstanding physical or historical characteristics has endowed the country with a vast reservoir of Spanish and Guaraní place-names. The upland campo upon which the colony's urban center was founded was called, for unknown reasons, La Colmena. The name was applied first to the new town and later to the entire settlement. The Japanese also accepted local names for major topographic and hydrographic features and added none of their own.[10]

The land purchased by the colonization company was divided into six zones, utilizing the north-flowing creeks as boundaries, and these were further subdivided into a total of 485 agricultural lots. The colony survey followed the characteristic rectilinear pattern; roads were aligned with the cardinal compass points, and property lines were laid out both parallel and at right angles to them. However, Japanese surveyors freely deviated from geometrical consistency in the face of topographic reality, and lots vary widely in size and detail of shape; lots average approximately 48 acres but range from 18 to 76 acres (Figure 26).

Most rural properties were surveyed in the form of strips 180 × 1,500 yards, the longest dimension extending across the interfluve surfaces perpendicular to their general trend. The intent was to distribute land equitably in terms of quality as well as to provide properties with running water. In addition, each colonist was assured a location on one of the principal roads. Near the foot of the Cerro Apitaguá this pattern was disrupted by topographic irregularities, and in Mbocayaty it was abandoned altogether.

In planning the settlement, provision was made for a planta urbana (town site) in which to establish the colony administration, and a hospital, schools, and marketing facilities. Originally the town was to be conveniently located near the center of the

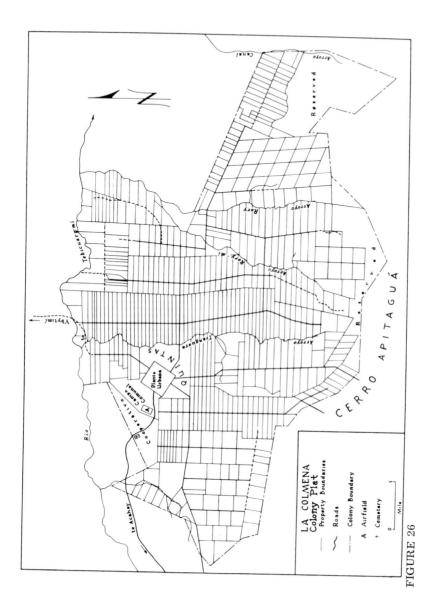

LA COLMENA
Colony Plat

Property Boundaries

— Roads
--- Colony Boundary
▲ Airfield
+ Cemetery

0 _____ 1
Mile

FIGURE 26

87

settlement, but it was moved westward to the area of upland campo to obviate the necessity of clearing the forest. The town plat resembles that of many small Paraguayan rural communities—wide streets intersect in the form of a grid with a plaza at the center. In La Colmena, however, the plaza is too small to serve anything but a decorative function; the church and other public facilities are located several blocks to the south and west. Plaza corners are oriented in the direction of the cardinal compass points, and streets extend in a NE - SW and NW - SE direction. A zone of irregularly shaped quintas was created around all but the western margin of the town.[11] Lowland campo to the west is reserved as common pasture.

In October, 1936, colonists began to arrive, and the original nucleus of settlers assumed the leadership and administration of the colony. The precise number of immigrants is difficult to determine. Before World War II most Japanese apparently emigrated in family groups, and for statistical purposes the family was considered as the basic immigration unit.[12] Estimates for families entering La Colmena range from 100 to 147. The most reliable source indicates that, between 1936 and 1941, 138 families consisting of 844 individuals formed the original colony.[13] Of these, 15 families totaling 54 persons were administrators, teachers, and other nonagriculturists. Colonists were recruited from throughout Japan, but most of them came from the northern and central part of the country.[14] In addition, 12 Japanese families were brought from pioneer zones in southern Brazil and distributed throughout the colony.

In spite of the investment in planning and preparation, the Japanese settlers encountered a variety of problems, which materially affected the growth of the settlement and conditioned many of the processes responsible for its present morphology. Like other foreign colonists in Paraguay, the Japanese were forced to contend with continual political unrest, a primitive economic structure, and poorly developed internal communications. However, the establishment of a stable and permanent settlement was inhibited by additional difficulties. The occupational structure of the immigrant group apparently included few of the skills suitable for tropical agricultural pioneering. According to informants no more than 40 percent were originally full-time farmers. Most colonists claimed to have worked occasionally on the farms of relatives, and two received some form of technical agricultural training, but the majority had little direct experience in agriculture. A doctor and a teacher were purposely

included and were encouraged to pursue their professions in
the colony.

The arrival of the colonists was also poorly timed. The
necessity for clearing the land and building shelters delayed
planting until after the appropriate season, and the first harvest
was meager. During the next several years reported outbreaks
of malaria severely reduced the labor force, and natural disasters and the failure of imported seed varieties further retarded
the development of a firm economic base.[15]

The survival of the colony was undoubtedly secured by a
common sense of purpose, perhaps related to larger Japanese
national ends, and by the presence of an authoritarian company
administration that directed colony life and represented a
tangible link with the mother country.[16] Colonists disagree on
the extent of administration control. Land was assigned arbitrarily, but colonists were permitted to establish themselves
immediately on their own parcels and to prepare them for
agriculture. However, the administration assumed a number of
economic prerogatives, which more or less enforced a close
association between colonists and the company. Settlers were
instructed what, where, when, and how much to plant. A company store dispensed tools, fertilizer, insecticides, and seed
as well as clothing, utensils, and small luxury items of Japanese
manufacture. The company also owned all facilities for processing and marketing of harvests (a rice mill, cotton gin, warehouse,
etc.).

The administration expected colonists to contribute labor
toward community projects such as the building of roads, a
school, and a hospital. In addition, it provided the only mechanism
for the solution of individual or collective problems and served
as an intermediary between the settlers and Paraguayan government officials. The degree to which the administration served as
an integrating and unifying force among the colonists is debatable.
A visitor to the settlement in 1937 observed:

> They [the colonists] were not yet free, but they did not understand the
> meaning of freedom. They planted when they were told to plant, what they
> were told to plant, and where they were told to plant it. Accordingly their
> crops thrived, and in this way they must thrive also.
> The organization . . . seemed perfect and happy.[17]

However, there is ample evidence that the organization was far
from perfect and certainly not entirely happy. Informants com-
plain that the organization was too complex and was subject to

constant and arbitrary direction from Japan. Considerable waste resulted from the construction of useless industrial facilities and the ultimately abandoned road to Ybytymí. Furthermore, the administration insisted on introducing an agricultural regimen based upon Brazilian colonization experience. Unfortunately, climatic contrasts proved to be marked, and several years were wasted before the relatively inflexible administration yielded to the practical experience of its colonists. Unquestionably, mismanagement caused considerable friction, which ultimately manifested itself in resistance not only to the administration but to organized cooperative effort of any kind.

The entrance of Japan into World War II greatly amplified the problems of the colonists. Almost immediately connections with the homeland were severed, and hoped-for reinforcement never materialized. In addition, Paraguayan authorities assumed control of the settlement, and from 1943 to 1947 the colonists were subject in all their activities to local Paraguayan police; the Japanese-language school was closed, and pioneers were forbidden to meet, or to leave the colony. Furthermore, the company administration was unable to finance the continued development of the settlement, and its influence over the colonists declined rapidly. In 1944, La Colmena became incorporated into the Paraguayan administrative framework as a distrito, and in 1948 a voluntary agricultural cooperative acquired all assets of the previous administration.

Although these setbacks retarded the development of the colony, the energy and the enterprise of its members have provided a continuous if modest growth. The relative progress of La Colmena is reflected in significant changes in the relationship of the colony to the region of which it is now a part, as well as by a profound metamorphosis in the settlement itself. The Japanese intended to support themselves in their new environment through commercial agriculture; the organized effort to produce surpluses, coupled with the energy with which pioneers pursued this activity, contrasted sharply with less concentrated economic effort in nearby native settlements.

Thus La Colmena, although not particularly thriving in comparison with Japanese settlements elsewhere in South America, has evolved as the regional focus of the area to which it was once peripheral. Indicative of this change is the effect of the colony upon regional patterns of population distribution. In 1936 the area contained fewer than 250 permanent residents; at present, some 3,100 people reside within the colony borders.[18] Because most of this growth has been at the expense of older population clusters in the vicinity, the ethnic content of the settlement has been drastically altered. The present strength of the Japanese cultural ingredient is difficult to determine accurately. A count by the administration in 1946 produced 137 families consisting of 793 persons. By 1956 the number of Japanese families had declined to approximately 120. The net decrease is apparently a consequence of abandonment by dissatisfied colonists.[19] The residue left by the operation of biological processes and migration consists of approximately 716 individuals who currently constitute about 20 percent of the total population of the colony (Table 6). It is worth noting that the majority of these were born in Paraguay.

TABLE 6

Movement of Population in La Colmena, 1936 - 1957

Population	No. of Families	No. of Individuals
Entered colony before 1941	138	844
Entered colony after 1955	9	53
Marriages and establishment of branch families	67	...
Births	...	475
SUBTOTAL:	214	1,372
Left colony	94	552[a]
Deaths	...	104
SUBTOTAL:	94	656
Total currently residing in colony:	120[b]	716[c]

Source: Usui (1958), pp. 147-148.

[a]According to Usui's chart (pp. 288-292), the 94 families leaving the colony consisted of only 520 individuals.
[b]Includes 27 branch families established in La Colmena.
[c]The total arrived at by Usui is 719 (p. 148).

The cessation of immigration in 1941 and the subsequent abandonment of the colony by a significant percentage of Japanese colonists left vacant a large number of rural properties. Many colonists took this opportunity to purchase additional land. Yet after colonists had exhausted their resources, more than one half of the colony land remained unoccupied, and Paraguayans began to acquire rural lots. By 1958, when all available land had been sold, Paraguayans emerged as the predominant land-holders. Of the 485 agricultural parcels, Paraguayans now occupy 322. Because Paraguayans began to settle in La Colmena primarily after the Japanese had become firmly established, most of the available land was located on the less accessible and less cultivable periphery, and it is here that the major concentrations of Paraguayan ownership developed. The marked preference of the Japanese for forest rather than campo has helped to accentuate the marginal location of Paraguayans who have no such prejudices (Figure 27).

The influx of Paraguayans has produced more profound changes in the character of the planta urbana. In the colony's formative years it served as an administrative center with few other functions. As productivity increased, Paraguayans were attracted to the settlement by possibilities of employment as farm laborers or in incipient agricultural industries, and growth in the number of wage earners stimulated a concomitant expansion in the provision of goods and services. In 1959 the town, with approximately 1,100 inhabitants, contained a disproportionate percentage of the colony population, suggesting that its influence extends beyond the borders of the settlement. It is here also that the predominance of the Paraguayan ethnic element is most notable. A few immigrants moved to town in the hope that commerce would prove more lucrative than agriculture, but urban residents of Japanese ancestry, including those living on suburban quintas, number less than 75.

It is apparent that La Colmena, at least from the Paraguayan point of view, has achieved its desired goals. All available land is occupied and the settlement itself is stable and productive. The influx of Paraguayans has relegated the foreign element to a distinct minority, and in the process, a relatively realistic balance has been preserved between ethnic origin and land-ownership. In the planta urbana, the Japanese constitute 6 percent of the population and control less than 15 percent of the property. In the rural zone, the 26 percent of the inhabitants who

LA COLMENA

Land Ownership

Japanese ▨

Paraguayan ☐

0 ___ 1
Mile

FIGURE 27

93

are of Japanese ancestry own approximately 36 percent of the land. But although the Japanese have been numerically submerged, they continue to provide the impetus necessary for the colony's economy.

As a feature of the Paraguayan landscape, La Colmena exhibits a complex of indigenous and introduced forms. In the course of its evolution it has acquired many of the characteristics of typical Paraguayan settlements. The colony's urban focus in particular is superficially almost indistinguishable from native rural communities. In the surrounding agricultural zone, however, the pioneer origins of La Colmena are clearly discernible. The regularity of land subdivision and uniformity of settlement contrast sharply with Paraguayan settlements in which slow and irregular accretion has been the principal growth mechanism. In addition, and of greater significance to the present work, there remains ample tangible evidence of the cultural antecedence of the immigrant colonists. In the paragraphs that follow, the settlement forms and activities of the Japanese pioneers are described in an effort to assess their impact upon the genesis and evolution of the cultural landscape. These data provide the basis for isolation and analysis of factors responsible for cultural conservatism as well as for processes of change.

THE SETTLEMENT PATTERN

La Colmena was planned as an agrarian community in which immigrant families were to acquire, develop, and occupy relatively large parcels of land. The resultant pattern of dispersed settlement seems at first glance to conflict with the predilection in rural Japan for agglomerated settlement—particularly as several basic elements of Japanese social behavior are greatly dependent upon the proximity of neighbors.

The process of selecting the settlement pattern is obscure. In planning La Colmena, the Japanese undoubtedly drew upon their experience in Brazil in order to produce a pattern that was both consistent with rural Paraguayan forms and recognizable as a proper colony by Paraguayan authorities. However, there is no evidence that the Japanese would have altered the settlement plan had they been entirely free to do so. On the contrary, colonists fully accept the pattern;[20] there is little inclination toward agglomeration even when the opportunity arises. Farmsteads are rarely within sight of each other, and there is no tendency among farmers to utilize the town as a residence, even when fields are adjacent. Most Japanese living in the planta urbana own agricultural properties, but all these properties are leased, consigned to an overseer, or loaned to relatives.

The placement of farmsteads on individual properties follows no consistent pattern. The system of colony roads seems to be the principal determinant in the location of dwellings and associated buildings. All parcels are either crossed or bounded by a road, and farmsteads are usually placed between 50 and 150 yards from it. Almost never are they immediately adjacent to the road, particularly if it is well traveled. Colonists in possession of relatively square lots have tended to locate farmsteads near the center of their property.

STRUCTURE PATTERNS

Immediately upon arrival, the Japanese were required to occupy their parcels and to erect some form of provisional shelter. Unfortunately, cultivation and work on colony projects monopolized pioneer energies, and although wealthier and more industrious pioneers were able to construct substantial dwellings, the majority were forced initially to occupy exceedingly rudimentary structures of bamboo and thatch.

A second phase of construction coincided with the entry of Japan into World War II. By 1941 colony-wide projects requiring group labor were largely completed, and the war cut the flow of capital for new projects. By this time also, plantations were extended to relatively stable limits imposed by market conditions and the colonists' own productive capabilities. With reduced obligations and increased capital, colonists intending to remain in La Colmena undertook construction of permanent dwellings. A few provisional shelters were preserved as auxiliary buildings or expanded into more substantial structures, but most of them were abandoned. Although several prosperous colonists have already replaced their second dwelling with a third, houses built between 1939 and 1943 remain the basic feature of the rural landscape.

The typical farmstead consists of one or at most two structures. More prosperous colonists have constructed specialized buildings as the scope of their operations has increased. Few farmers have more than two buildings, and some remain content with one general structure that combines living, storage, and other functions.

Buildings preserve many recognizably Japanese characteristics but are far from homogeneous in morphology. The colonization company offered no architectural guidelines. Several carpenters were included in the roster of settlers, but their skills, which might have standardized building patterns, were not generally utilized. Variations in size, upkeep, and adornment represent not only the degree of economic success of the colonists, but also economic and perhaps class differentiation inherited from Japan. Most colonists were of relatively modest means, but several managed to accumulate substantial capital from the sale of property and belongings in Japan. Adequate financial resources did not necessarily insure success; those accustomed to financial management, and with money to hire labor, were able to begin operations on a larger scale and to acquire greater and more rapid returns. A part of these returns was usually invested in building, both in an attempt to bring living up to accustomed standards and as a mark of status.

Structures are also subject to limited stylistic variation. Whereas in Japan, rural construction is still characterized by a number of regionally distinctive patterns, among La Colmena settlers there is no specific regional concentration. Lack of traditional building materials and the demands of pioneer living have also served to limit stylistic expression. The range of variation in architectural elements is restricted to several basic patterns adapted from the simpler structural modes typical of rural southern and central Japan.

In plan, dwellings are rectangular, with the proportions of length to width depending upon the number of rooms required. Interconnecting rectangular units forming the L-, T-, or U-shaped structures so characteristic of Japanese farmsteads are rare. Although compass direction apparently influences house orientation in some parts of rural Japan, no such tendency is observable in La Colmena.[21]

The organization of interior space exhibits a wider range of choice in detail. Rooms are of all sizes and are not standardized by the dimensions of the tatami (floor mat). Two basic room arrangements are typical: (1) In 60 percent of the houses visited the entrance opens upon a small dirt-floored area at one end intended for reception of visitors but also commonly containing cooking facilities. The remainder of the dwelling is provided with a raised wooden floor compartmentalized by partitions extending three quarters of the distance to the beams supporting the roof. Ceilings are absent except in the rare houses where a second story has been added. (2) In several dwellings the entrance, near the center of the structure, opens upon a dirt-floored reception room separating wood-floored living quarters at one end from cooking and storage facilities at the other.

Three farmhouses have partial second stories entered by interior stairways. The upper floors were intended as sleeping quarters in an effort "to escape mosquitoes," but they apparently no longer function as such.[22] In one house the second floor is no longer habitable (Figure 28; see also Figure 31, p. 100).

Roofs are supported in Japanese fashion by a framework of horizontal, squared beams joined to vertical supports by means

FIGURE 28

Dwelling of K. Miamoto. The partial second story, built originally as a dormitory, is no longer utilized. Eucalyptus trees are conspicuous in the foreground. (The wooden object in center is a small sledge.)

of mortices and tenons. Thatch is normally used to cover the bamboo grid that is lashed to supporting beams. Traditional Japanese thatching materials did not prove durable under local climatic conditions, and colonists quickly adopted the native grasses used by Paraguayans. Thatch was applied in the typical Japanese fashion. Thick bundles of grass or straw were lashed to the grid with rope or vine, then straightened, and cut or beaten into a smooth surface. In most cases the last step was done cursorily or omitted altogether, and resultant roofs averaged more than a foot in thickness. According to informants, thick roofs proved conducive to rapid decay, and in recent construction, thatch has been gradually reduced to Paraguayan proportions or abandoned in favor of tile.

Roof style closely resembles standard Japanese yosemune patterns, which are common in southern and central Honshu and predominant in Kyushu.[23] In La Colmena the pyramidal yosemune roof slopes steeply upward to the longitudinal crest, which is protected by a bulge of thatch held in place by strips of bamboo wired or lashed to its surface (Figure 29). The decorative thatch-holding devices occasionally associated with this style are absent. A second common form has less pitch and lacks the elevated crest (Figure 30). Several rural dwellings possess gabled roofs, but these appear to be expedient adaptations of simple Paraguayan forms rather than conscious efforts to reproduce the kirizuma, or Japanese gable.

FIGURE 29

Farmstead of A. Kasamatsu. The structure at left was completed after the war and serves exclusively as a dwelling. The original building continues to serve storage and cooking functions as well as housing younger children and visitors.

FIGURE 30

Farmstead of R. Seki. Exterior walls are faced with split bamboo to
prevent washing of mud plaster. Bananas and other fruit trees surround
the dwelling. Land in foreground is in fallow after more than 10 years
of continuous cultivation.

Walls are constructed between vertical beams buried in the
ground at regular intervals. However, enclosure is accomplished
in several ways. The Japanese method of keying a bamboo grid to
beams by grooves or notches is widely employed. This lattice is
intended to receive a thin layer of mud plaster inside and out,
leaving vertical beams exposed. Such walls have not proved
durable, and, in the absence of pronounced roof overhang, must
be protected from weathering by vertical strips of split bamboo
(Figure 30). Plastering apparently proved too time-consuming,
and on many houses the final coat of smooth fine plaster has been
omitted. A few farmers have built walls of vertical logs in the
Paraguayan fashion for protection and privacy until plastering
could be accomplished. Wooden planks have also been used
occasionally, and in rare instances plank and plaster have been
combined (Figure 31).

In other architectural details, Japanese influence is less
discernible. A small porch protecting the principal entrance is
obviously Japanese (Figure 31), but only three houses have one,

FIGURE 31

Two-story dwelling combining most of the construction techniques and styles common in La Colmena. The wall at right remains unplastered. Note the small garden at left.

and the long narrow porches characteristic of many Japanese farmhouses are absent. Windows are small and rectangular and are often patterned after Japanese types; there is, however, considerable variety in choice of shape and closure.

Dwelling interiors preserve few Japanese traits. Almost all residences have raised wooden floors, but these are usually restricted to sleeping quarters. In later buildings, wooden floors have been continually reduced in area and are apparently rapidly disappearing in favor of packed earth or tile. Cooking is done in a dirt-floored room on raised clay fireplaces, and meals are taken in the same area except when visitors are present. A small iron charcoal brazier identical with that used by Paraguayans is commonly used to heat water for tea or maté, but the standard hibachi is absent. Neither separate cooking sheds nor the typical Paraguayan outdoor oven were observed.[24] Informants indicated that some families possessed Paraguayan-style log mortars, but none were observed. Furnishings are limited to chairs, tables, and beds of simple Paraguayan manu-

facture and, among more prosperous colonists, a sewing machine.
The household shrines (<u>Butsudan,</u> <u>Kamidana</u>) are present in perhaps half the homes.

Outbuildings, where present, are of several types. Toilet
facilities are located near dwellings in groves of trees or
bamboo but are built with little care because human wastes
are not collected for fertilizer. Japanese-style baths are still
in use by some colonists and are usually located within the main
dwelling. Buildings intended for storage of crops, seed, and
tools are usually enclosed sheds, but Paraguayan <u>galpónes</u>
(shelters), consisting only of roofs, are common. As few animals
are kept, little or no shelter is provided for them.

Pioneer structures retain sufficient evidence of Japanese
tradition to form a distinctive ingredient in the cultural landscape.
Yet it is obvious that introduced patterns have been compromised
in various ways. The general problem of cultural processes and
their relationship to the landscape is the subject of the conclusion
to the present work, but it is cogent to consider here some of
the circumstances that may have influenced changes in patterns
of construction.

La Colmena was intentionally established in an isolated and
sparsely peopled region. Entering colonists, exposed to a few of
the simplest rural Paraguayan structural modes, found little
worth imitating and were under no pressure to do so. Clearly,
the general intent was to recreate traditional living patterns.
However, as noted earlier, in the initial phase of settlement few
colonists could afford or were permitted to devote their principal
energies to problems of shelter. Apparently, also, typical patterns of house-building cooperation do not appear to have functioned effectively, owing to the recent formation of the group, its
heterogeneous regional and social composition, and the separation
of its members through dispersed settlement.

Thus, colonists were forced to rely upon their own often
severely limited resources of time, energy, capital, and skill.
Because few of the Japanese had previously faced the problem of
designing and constructing dwellings, the reservoir of skills
was neither large nor particularly diverse.

The shortage of skills was compounded by difficulties in
obtaining traditional furnishings and building materials. The
standardized <u>tatami</u> was apparently considered inappropriate
for pioneering; it was not introduced, nor was its manufacture
attempted. Most colonists brought Japanese-style bedding, but

original stocks were impossible to replace when worn out. Saw-
timber for floors, paneling, and other elements of Japanese
carpentry was (and is) in short supply. The company administration established a sawmill but monopolized its meager output
for colony-wide projects. Several colonists used pit-saws to process the timber from their own land, but production was limited.

These factors have served to reduce construction to extreme
functional simplicity. In the process, most forms have been con-
densed to a nearly irreducible minimum, and several of the most
characteristic features of Japanese rural architecture have been
eliminated entirely. The roof is still considered the dwelling's
most basic element, and colonists appear reluctant to alter
traditional styles and techniques. However, the nearly universal
preference for the yosemune style is a logical consequence of
simplification. The yosemune, or its variations, is widespread
in Japan, and although it can be elaborate, the basic form requires a minimum of technology, is adaptable to a wide variety
of materials, and can be constructed with the labor resources of
an average family. Walls reflect a similar emphasis upon basic
essentials. Time-consuming Japanese methods of constructing
mud-plaster walls were attempted by more than half of the
colonists, but these were rarely completed, and simpler but more
durable forms have been adopted as additions were made or other
structures built.

In dwelling interiors, economy of effort and materials is even
more evident. Most structures were originally designed to serve
more than one function. Need for storage and work space has
reduced the size and changed the pattern of the actual living area.
Raised wooden floors are limited to sleeping quarters, and concomitant elements such as the central fire pit, which in Japan
serves as a family social center as well as for cooking, have
been eliminated. Where outbuildings now assume storage and
shop functions, living area has expanded, but dirt floors and
western furnishings prevail. Where interior space has been subdivided, partitioning screens, sliding doors, and other elements
of sophisticated carpentry have been totally abandoned.

Postponement of construction of permanent dwellings for
two to five years undoubtedly stimulated several other changes.
The prolonged sacrifice to expediency of traditional elements—
particularly those with little functional utility—accustomed
colonists to their absence. Certainly there has been no evident
attempt to re-establish discarded traits. Indeed, the trend is

toward more severe simplicity than circumstances require. The
delay also provided increased opportunity to absorb experience.
Early experiments with thatch and plaster indicated that Japanese methods yielded unsatisfactory results, and modifications
have appeared when such tasks must be repeated.

Possibilities for adoption of essentially Paraguayan techniques were also greatly enhanced. In rural construction the
Japanese and Paraguayans share several fundamental concepts,
and once colonists had become conditioned to functional simplicity they evidently began to find acceptable substitutes in materials and methods. As farms began to yield cash incomes,
colonists found it possible to hire native labor. Paraguayans had
no appreciable impact upon strongly held convictions, such as
proper roof form. However, communication was difficult, and
it often proved simpler to permit laborers to utilize their own
tools and techniques.

Transformations in rural architectural traditions have pro-
ceeded slowly. Since 1936 changes have had little opportunity to
develop beyond the effects of initial reactions to shortage, hardship, and lack of experience. Most colonists still inhabit early
structures, which do not incorporate the influences of additional
years of pioneering. However, many dwellings now show the
effects of age, and their owners face the problem of replacement.
It is reasonable to assume that this background of experience
will be expressed in new and more drastic departures from
original traditions. Four pioneer families have actually built
their third house. Unfortunately, their situations connot be considered typical, but the material evidence of modification may
be indicative of the degree, direction, and rate of change.

For three of the four families, surrender to local tradition
has been complete. However, structures are copies of small,
brick-and-tile buildings characteristic of urban environments
rather than duplications of less substantial rural dwellings
(Figure 32). Furnishings are western, and there is no evidence
of the survival of Japanese traits. Two of the three families
are related (father and son) but all are financially successful
and occupy lots adjacent to the town of La Colmena. It is perhaps more than coincidental that the three families were among
those brought from Brazil as experienced pioneers.

The fourth dwelling, that of the colony's largest landholder,[25]
represents a complex fusion of introduced and native elements.
The house, which is still not entirely complete, is built of brick,

FIGURE 32

Dwelling of Sr. Owara, completed in 1958, modeled after brick-and-plaster house of a type common in Paraguayan rural towns. Owara is head of one of the families from Brazil.

finely plastered and neatly whitewashed in the interior. The gabled roof is supported in the Paraguayan fashion. More pitch is used than is common in Paraguay, but the thatch is no thicker than that of well-made Paraguayan roofs, except that the crest is protected by a noticeable bulge of thatch held in place with longitudinal bamboo poles. Mortice and tenon joints are used in all carpentry. Occasionally large curved beams support interior walls, and their heavily shellacked surfaces are attractively exposed through the plaster. The rectangular floor plan is divided into five rooms with the kitchen at one end and the entrance and reception room near the center. The reception room is without a ceiling and in summer is converted into a breezeway by the opening of two pairs of wide doors that extend to the roof. Floors are of brick or tile, and all furnishings are patterned after western styles.

In the planta urbana, two brick buildings constructed for the doctor suggest Japanese influence in the form of their tile roofs. All other Japanese in the urban nucleus live in Paraguayan-style houses, and the one residence of obvious Japanese origin has been abandoned to a Paraguayan family. Paraguayan-style houses occupied by Japanese are outwardly indistinguishable from others, except for an occasional well-kept vegetable garden and, in two homes, a goldfish pond.

LIVELIHOOD PATTERNS

The law permitting Japanese to enter Paraguay firmly committed them to agriculture and further specified that the colonists were to produce "for export." Immigrants were presumably selected on the basis of farming experience, and the survey, settlement, and management of the colony were designed to facilitate commercial agriculture. About three fifths of the first planting was devoted to crops intended for sale, and the proportion of land in cash crops has continually increased. Today, 95 families of Japanese ancestry devote their entire energies to farming, and more than 75 percent of their land is utilized for commercial crops.

Agriculture

1. LAND TENURE   Paraguayan Japanese possess a strong predilection for landownership. The company expected to profit from the sale of land, and outright ownership has emerged as the only significant form of tenure. By 1958, 75 percent of the Japanese had acquired full title to their land, and the remainder were in the process of doing so.[26]

The company, anticipating the settlement of one family per lot, considered 50 acres as the optimum farming unit and surveyed the land accordingly. However, the Japanese have purchased additional land whenever the opportunity has arisen. Colonists possessing sufficient initial capital acquired compact holdings through purchase of adjacent lots, but most farmers were forced to delay acquisition for several years, and disjunct ownership patterns are common.

Table 7 lists ownership characteristics for eighty farmers who control 144 of the 163 lots owned by Japanese. Multiple ownership amounts to 68 percent of the total acreage. The

fifteen colonists owning three or more lots account for 43 percent of the land. The smallest farm (excluding quintas) consists
of a single parcel containing 31.4 acres. The largest farm contains nine lots totaling 518.7 acres. The average of 75 acres is
smaller than pioneer farms elsewhere in Paraguay but is almost twice that of native farmers owning land in La Colmena.

Motivations for acquisition of additional land are listed below;
the order is not intended as a measure of relative importance:

a. Land inequality: Almost all lots include land that cannot
be cultivated, and on some lots as much as 30 percent of the
surface cannot be farmed. Owners of such properties have often
sought to acquire others.

b. Expansion: Some colonists, particularly the more successful ones, consider 50 acres too small a sphere for their activities
and have purchased additional land for expansion of plantations.

c. Diversification: Dissatisfaction with current crop patterns
has prompted acquisition of land suitable for other pursuits. The
colony's largest landholder recently bought 250 acres of campo for
production of rice and cattle.

d. Investment: During World War II, colonists were unable to
spend surplus funds on improvements or luxuries, and many of
them invested in land. Profit seems to have been a minor consideration. Many colonists expressed the view that virgin forest
was "money in the bank"—a necessary reserve for the ultimate
replacement of lands depleted through continuous cultivation.

TABLE 7

Ownership Characteristics of Eighty Japanese Farmers in
La Colmena

No. of Lots Owned	No. of Farmers	Total Lots	Area (acres)
1	47	47	2,282
2	18	36	1,840
3	10	30	1,445
4	1	4	188
5	1	5	272
6	1	6	297
7	1	7	356
9	1	9	519
TOTAL:	80	144	7,199

e. Inheritance and/or the establishment of branch families:
As in Japan, colonists still do not believe in subdividing family
patrimony by inheritance, but the obligation to provide a future
in the colony for sons or siblings is keenly felt.[27] Aid to branch
families varies with individual capabilities, but land amounting
to one lot is considered adequate. When no land is available the
family head usually contributes toward education or finds some
other way to assist.

f. Ownership satisfaction: The possibility of owning large
quantities of land in South America was undoubtedly the major
stimulus for the migration of some Japanese. Although the evidence is far from conclusive, the residual tendency of a few
colonists to equate land with wealth suggests that the traditional
relation between landownership and social status may have been
transferred to Paraguay.

2. CROP PATTERNS   In more than 25 years, less than half the
land owned by Japanese has been brought under cultivation. Expectably, the size of individual plantations is roughly proportional
to the size of total holdings. Owners of one parcel average 17
acres of cultivated land. Owners of more than one lot cultivate
from 25 to 90 acres. The failure to develop holdings more fully
reflects early difficulties in becoming established. Problems of
marketing, shortages of labor, and variations in the number of
potential laborers per family have also tended to limit agricultural
activities. An additional if less tangible factor involves the conflict between traditional Japanese agricultural attitudes and techniques and the realities of Paraguay's near-tropical environment.
The Japanese penchant for clean tillage is alone sufficient to
restrict the scope of farming activities. However, the over-all
intensity of Japanese agriculture, although compromised to
some degree, places limits upon the amount of land that can be
cultivated.

Crop patterns have remained relatively stable throughout the
history of the colony. The selection of principal crops in the
association was greatly influenced by the colonization company
and its successor, the colony cooperative. Within this framework of informal and ill-defined controls, farmers exercise
individual preferences, and plantations vary somewhat in detail
(Table 8).

TABLE 8

Crop Patterns of Selected Farmers, 1951 - 1956 (in acres)

Farmer	Total Acres	Cotton	Rice	Maize	Mandioca	Peanuts	Beans	Onions	Sugar-cane	Wheat	Tobacco	Perennial	Other	Total Cultivated
Miamoto														
1951	148	25	1	5	3	0.7	5	...	...	...	...	0.5	...	40.2
1952	148	25	0.5	6	2.5	1	2.5	...	...	...	...	...	0.5	38
1953	148	32	1	5	5	3	6	...	...	...	5	1	...	60
1954[a]	148													
1955	148	20	...	5	2.5	...	5	3	...	...	...	...	2	37.5
1956	148	20	...	2.5	10	2	...	...	...	...	...	1	1	36.5
Mitue														
1951	250	61	5	25	5	2.5	2.5	...	...	...	...	2	...	103
1952	321	61	1.8	25	10	2.5	7	...	...	...	...	0.5	8	115.8
1953	321	49	1	20	7	2.5	12	2	...	1	2.5	0.5	1	98.5
1954[a]	321													
1955	371	14	2.5	5	2.5	1	3	2.5	2.5	1	1	0.5	...	35.5
1956	519	30	3	2.5	7	4.5	...	...	2.5	...	...	0.5	1	51
Nakayama														
1951	98	25	2.5	2.5	12	2.5	5	...	...	...	...	2.5	...	52
1952	98	25	...	5	10	2.5	2.5	...	...	...	...	2.5	...	47.5
1953	148	20	...	3.5	6	1	2.5	...	...	...	...	2.5	5	41.5
1954	198	30	2.5	2.5	7	2.5	2.5	3.5	...	1	2.5	5	...	58
1955	272	25	5	2.5	2.5	...	2.5	4	...	2	...	2.5	...	45
1956	272	37	4	5	4.5	...	4	4	...	...	...	2	...	62.5
R. Seki														
1951	49	14	0.5	2.5	0.1	0.5	3	...	...	...	...	0.5	...	21.1
1952	49	12	...	7	2.5	1.5	0.5	...	...	...	...	2	...	25.5
1953	49	7	...	2.5	1.5	0.7	2.5	...	...	...	...	...	...	14.2
1954	49	7	...	2	2	0.2	2.5	1.5	...	...	2	...	...	17.2
1955	49	7	0.5	2.5	1	0.5	2.5	1	...	...	...	1	...	16
1956	49	8	0.5	5	1	1	1	1	...	0.5	...	1	...	15

Source: MS records of Cooperativa La Colmena, S R L.

[a]No crop data obtainable.

Since 1936 cotton has been the dominant crop in acreage and value. During the first agricultural year (1937 - 1938), 465 of an approximate total of 1,240 cultivated acres were devoted to cotton.[28] In 1956 the crop accounted for 1,000 of the 2,500 acres farmed by the eighty Japanese members of the cooperative.[29] The rationale behind the selection of this particular crop by the company is obscure. Cotton is common in Japanese colonies in Peru and Brazil, and it is possible that prewar Japanese planners anticipated a steady flow of the commodity to the home textile industry from colonies overseas. Cotton is also traditional in Paraguayan agriculture, and the decision may have been based upon selection of a lucrative local crop with which company administrators possessed some experience.

Farmers have experimented extensively to find cotton varieties responsive to Paraguayan agricultural conditions. At present, several United States hybrids (acclimatized in Brazil) are most popular. Yields vary depending upon the length of time a given field has been under cultivation; for virgin forest soils, 1,300 lb. per acre are claimed. Land cultivated for 10 or more years yields less than 600 lb. per acre.

Although cotton is predominant, agriculture among pioneers is best described as polyculture. The multicrop system was apparently adopted in a conscious effort to avoid the risks of monoculture. Most colonists annually harvest at least five crops, and some of them harvest many more (Figures 33, 34, and 35). Important crops grown primarily for off-farm sale include maize, beans, onions, potatoes, peanuts, and tobacco.

Next to cotton, maize and beans are consistently the most profitable crops, and all farmers are engaged in their production. Although both crops are staples in native agriculture, production among Paraguayans is ill organized, and the Japanese have managed to acquire a share of the market. To improve their competitive position, colonists have increased yields with Brazilian hybrids.

Onions and potatoes were introduced in 1946. Their popularity was slow to develop, but a stable if small market exists within the country, and production has gradually increased. Although about two thirds of the colonists grow both crops, there remain some serious difficulties in their production. Colonists have failed to encounter seed varieties suited to local ecological conditions. Potatoes in particular are inconsistent producers, and climatic factors make storage difficult.

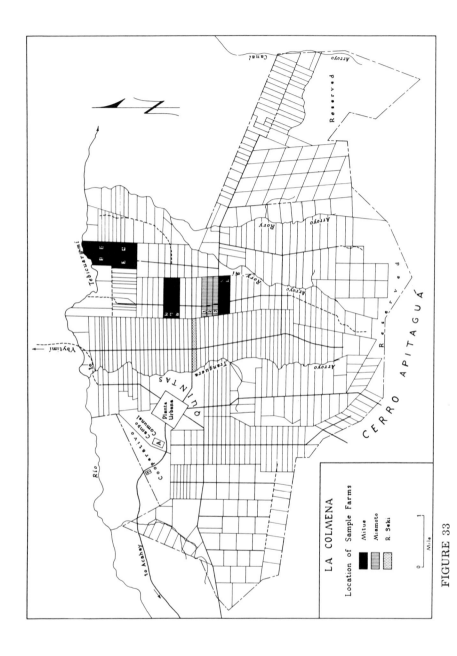

LA COLMENA

Location of Sample Farms

- ■ Mitue
- ▥ Minamoto
- ▦ R. Seki

0 — Mile — 1

FIGURE 33

110

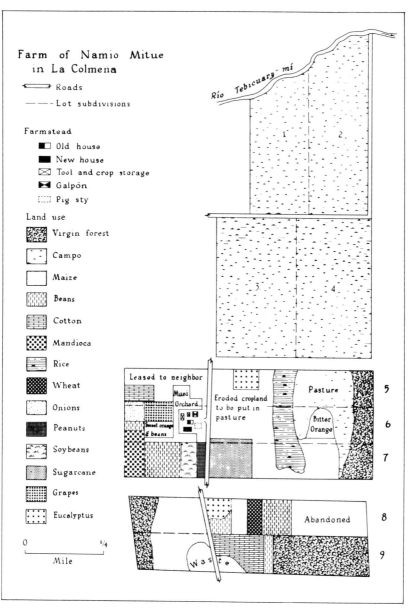

Farm of Namio Mitue
in La Colmena

Roads
———·Lot subdivisions

Farmstead
■◧ Old house
■ New house
⊠ Tool and crop storage
▶◀ Galpón
▦ Pig sty

Land use
Virgin forest
Campo
Maize
Beans
Cotton
Mandioca
Rice
Wheat
Onions
Peanuts
Soybeans
Sugarcane
Grapes
Eucalyptus

0   ¼
        Mile

Río Tebicuary-mí

1   2

3   4

Leased to neighbor

Mixed
Orchard

Sweet orange
& beans

Eroded cropland
to be put in
pasture

Pasture

Bitter
Orange

5

6

7

Abandoned

Waste

8

9

FIGURE 34

111

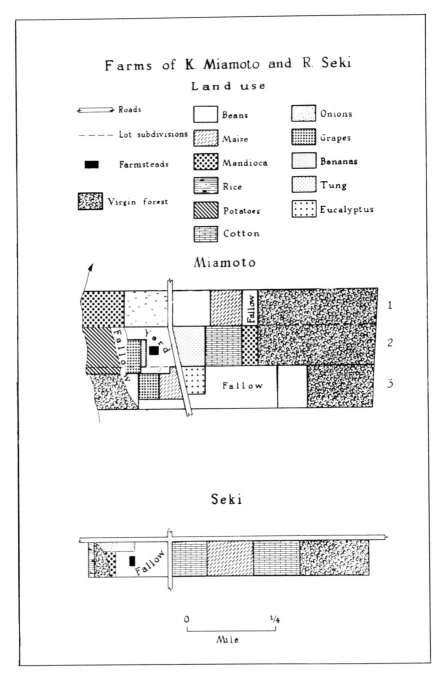

FIGURE 35

Both peanuts and tobacco have declined in importance. Peanuts are grown for oil, but there are no processing facilities in La Colmena. Tobacco, a traditional mainstay of Paraguayan commercial agriculture, was early selected by the administration for emphasis. By 1943, approximately 10 percent of the total area cultivated was devoted to tobacco; in 1956, less than 30 acres were planted.

In contrast to most foreign colonies in Paraguay, the culture of perennial crops never developed significantly. From the predominantly German pioneer zone near Villarrica the Japanese acquired yerba, tung, and grapes, as well as the rudiments of their cultivation. Of these, tung proved the most successful, and in 1946, 15 farmers reported a total of 11,600 trees. Recently, however, Paraguay has lost ground to other sources of tung oil; by 1956 there were only 4,500 trees, and no new plantings have been undertaken. In 1957, the colony cooperative established a winery and has encouraged members to plant grapes. In 1959, 58 farmers grew a total of 77 acres, and interest in the crop is apparently increasing. Several farmers have commercial plantings of sweet and bitter oranges, or both. The bitter orange in particular has passed through several cycles of popularity, and at one time pioneer farmers reported having more than 50,000 trees. However, few colonists are now willing to devote land to perennial crops involving such a high degree of uncertainty. Yerba, which provides the economic base for most pioneer agriculture in eastern Paraguay, was cultivated on a small scale, but conditions proved marginal, and plantings disappeared.

In addition to these crops, a wide variety of plants are grown that, although occasionally commercialized, are intended primarily for consumption within the colony. Most important of these is mandioca. Although totally foreign to Japanese agriculturists (except the families from Brazil), it readily became incorporated into pioneer dietary and farming patterns, and today approximately 90 percent of the settlers grow it. Individual plantings rarely exceed five acres, but heavy yields compensate for the small area cultivated.

Rice was perhaps the first crop planted in La Colmena. Upland varieties were initially introduced by the administration, which judged correctly that only a small amount of colony land was suitable for paddy cultivation and decided that labor and capital required to develop paddies could not be spared during the initial phases of settlement. Early outbreaks of malaria were an additional factor. The choice was also predicated upon the assumption that Paraguayan climatic conditions were analogous to those in pioneer zones of southeast Brazil. Unfortunately, unreliable rainfall made the growing of nonirrigated rice highly speculative, and after five years of frustrating failure, the crop was abandoned.

Today all rice is grown in irrigated paddies on terraces along the margins of the colony's principal watercourses. However, the number of colonists producing rice, as well as the area devoted to its cultivation, remains severely limited by the paucity of suitable land. In 1959, 60 acres were planted in paddies from which colonists met approximately half their annual needs.

Other field crops have been selected by a minority of farmers. Sweet potatoes are grown by nearly half of the colonists, but total acreage fluctuates markedly depending upon the commercial possibilities for surpluses. About 30 percent of the Japanese produce soybeans, used chiefly in the manufacture of shoyu (soy sauce). An equal number of them grow a small amount of sugarcane, most of which is fed to work animals. Small quantities of wheat and alfalfa are also planted by a few farmers.

In Table 9, acreages and yields of the principal crops are summarized for selected years. The data for 1955 were supplied by the colony cooperative and include plantations of 80 farmers who were members of the group in that year.

Several groups of plants cultivated by the Japanese are excluded from agricultural statistics. Almost every farm possesses a kitchen garden devoted to the production of a wide variety of vegetables, including lettuce, cabbages, beets, carrots, spinach, radishes, leeks, and tomatoes. Such vegetables, although entering into local barter and gift-exchange patterns, are intended primarily for home consumption. Around most farmsteads fruit trees are planted, particularly citrus and banana. Such trees are usually found in carefully planned orchards next to farmsteads.

Some colonists also devote small portions of their land to nonfood plants. Bamboo and timber trees are occasionally planted near farmsteads. In most cases these trees occupy "waste" land on road margins or field boundaries. However, several farmers possess eucalyptus groves covering several acres. Rank grasses are planted along the margins of interior field divisions for roof thatch. Plants grown strictly for ornament are conspicuous by their absence.

TABLE 9

Principal Crops for Selected Years in La Colmena

Field Crops (No. of acres)	1937[a]	1941	1945	1955[b]
Cotton	465	829	1,927	946
Maize	175	435	326	380
Mandioca	95	138	173	241
Rice	389[c]	170	54	64
Soybeans	64	148	44	25[d]
Other beans and peanuts	41	40	247	479[e]
Tobacco	0	22	257	27
Potatoes	0	0	17	34
Wheat	0	10	143	40
Sugarcane	0	0	0	24
Onions	0	17	22	178
Other[f]	15	45	550	175
TOTAL	1,244	1,854	3,760	2,613

Perennial Crops (No. of plants)	1937[a]	1941	1945	1955[b]
Tung	0	no data[f]	11,600	4,900
Grapes	0	no data	0	1,500
Sweet oranges	0	no data	10,350	7,000
Bitter oranges	0	no data	57,000	4,000
Other citrus fruit	0	no data	2,080	no data
Bananas	0	no data	5,238	no data
Pineapples	0	no data	375	no data
Coffee	0	no data	230	no data

Sources: MS records of Cooperativa La Colmena, SRL. Usui (1958). Moriya (1948).

[a] By the end of 1937 only 58 farm families had arrived.

[b] Data for 1955 included only 80 families who were members of the colony cooperative in that year.

[c] Mountain rice.

[d] Estimate.

[e] Peanuts, 104; other beans, 375.

[f] Includes principally sweet potatoes, vegetables, sunflowers (before 1950), and alfalfa.

It is apparent that crops selected provided little challenge to Japanese agricultural technology. With few exceptions, all plants ultimately stabilized in the complex were within the possible range of Japanese agricultural experience as well as being part of traditional Paraguayan agriculture. This coincidental correspondence precluded the necessity for pronounced adjustments on the part of Japanese farmers and materially reduced the possibilities for plant introductions from Japan. Only in household gardens are there uniquely Oriental plants such as daikon, the giant white radish, Chinese cabbage, and adzuki, a small bean used in sweets.

Japanese colonists have a well-developed sense of superiority concerning their agricultural capabilities in relation to those of Paraguayans; informants insist that they can "grow anything" and that economics rather than technology is the chief determinant of current crop-patterns. Only for tobacco does there seem to be a suggestion of cultural antipathy. To be sure, decline in production can be ascribed to economic factors. However, in addition to concern over high-loss risk and the high ratio of labor input, most informants expressed a personal "dislike" for the crop.

3. ANIMAL HUSBANDRY   The raising of livestock, which is one of the more important rural Paraguayan enterprises, is of almost no consequence in Japanese pioneer agriculture. The original purchase included little land suitable for grazing, and colonists, with almost no experience in animal husbandry, could not be convinced that campo lands within colony boundaries were worth purchasing. Rather, they preferred to invest in forest land that could be made quickly productive by clearing and planting—processes with which about half of the settlers were relatively familiar. As Paraguayans moving into the colony acquired the available grassland, possibilities for cattle raising became even more remote. Because animals are required for farm work and transportation, most colonists have been forced to acquire several oxen and horses. However, few possess more than this basic minimum, and provision for animals has had little effect upon colony agriculture. Only one colonist breeds cattle as a business.[30] A census of farm animals conducted in 1956 credits pioneers with 139 horses, 458 cattle (oxen?), 341 pigs, and 2,300 chickens.[31]

4. AGRICULTURAL PRACTICES

a. Labor: Prospective colonists were apparently judged by their capability for work, and once in the settlement they were expected to establish farms through their own effort. Labor was evidently massed for the initial clearing and planting of approximately 1,000 acres, but no other preparatory clearing or planting was undertaken, and although the administration did attempt to supply Paraguayan laborers there were few in the vicinity, and their supervision required the services of a company interpreter; more significantly, few colonists could afford them.

Migration of family units was promoted specifically to assure an adequate labor supply. From the beginning, however, family labor was exposed to severe pressures that have steadily increased the role of hired labor in colony productivity. Although statistics indicate a favorable family size for entering colonists, many families were apparently well below optimum strength.[32] Data for the 93 farm families now resident in the colony show that before World War II fully half of them consisted of four members or fewer, and that at least 20 "families" were represented by only one individual.

Even among large families, labor shortages apparently have occurred. The colony administration regularly recruited settlers for work on colony-wide projects.[33] In addition, malaria and other diseases periodically decimated the working population. Also, most children have been removed from participation in farm work by attendance at school. Traditional patterns of labor cooperation, which might have compensated for shortages, do not seem to have functioned effectively. Recent evidence indicates that cooperation is increasing as the mesh of family relationships becomes more intricate through intermarriage among the residue of permanent settlers. During the critical first decade the hastily constituted, heterogeneous group lacked the ties upon which such cooperation is normally based, and dispersed settlement further inhibited the development of mutual aid. A certain amount of neighborly help has been available, particularly for planting of rice, but such cooperation is far less formalized than in Japan.

There are no statistics to chart the growth of dependence upon hired labor. According to a consensus of colony leaders, about 40 percent of the human energy now expended in agriculture is provided by native laborers. Owners of large holdings employ

5 to 8 peons on a regular basis and as many as 35 during critical periods. Other farmers employ proportionately fewer, some
of them being able to afford help only on rare occasions. However,
all informants had at some time employed peons, and the only
restriction upon more extensive use of wage labor is apparently
economic.

Regular laborers live on or near the farm that is offering
employment and generally work on a year-round basis for meals
and a small wage. In addition, they are usually provided with a
small amount of land—1.5 acres if married, less if single. Larger
numbers of occasional laborers enter the colony when their
services are required. Occasional laborers are paid on a piece-
work basis for specific tasks, and all relationship to the employer
terminates upon completion of the job. Wages vary according to
the task, and for the planting of paddy, a job that Paraguayans
detest, colonists must pay double the ordinary wage (Figure 36).

In spite of the increasing amount of work relegated to hired
labor, Japanese colonists, unlike their German counterparts,
have tended to remain farmers. In older German colonies there
has been a notable shift away from personal participation in

FIGURE 36

Paraguayan laborers planting rice in a Japanese colonist's paddies.
Paraguayans demand extra pay for such work and usually must be
closely supervised by pioneer farmers.

production.[34] In La Colmena, almost all colonists work side by side with peons. Unlike the Germans, also, Japanese pioneers have not resorted to the "adoption" of homeless Paraguayan adolescents (criados) to augment family labor, even though there is apparently some cultural precedent for such behavior.[35]

b. Tools: The pioneer tool inventory is smaller and more generalized than is normal for Japanese farmers. Most colonists outfitted themselves with a basic minimum of agricultural implements before leaving for Paraguay, and convenience, cost, and advice from immigration officials functioned as selective factors. The colonization company further restricted the range of tool types available by importing only those of proved utility. The processes of elimination and consolidation are continuous. Several basic tools have generally been discarded as experience has demonstrated them to be superfluous. When the original imported tools have worn out, replacement has often been impractical or impossible, and colonists have been forced to substitute or to abandon them altogether.

Complexity of tool inventory depends to some extent upon the scope of individual operations (Figure 37). However, all colonists

FIGURE 37

N. Mitue, the colony's biggest landholder, with his basic tool assemblage. Not shown are a large number of hand-tools including Japanese saws and sickles.

put the general emphasis on hand-tools and most of them possess
the same basic complement. Axes, hoes, shovels, rakes, forks,
and sickles were imported but nearly all have undergone some
modifications. Hoes, in particular, have been reduced from the
variety of specialized Japanese forms to the heavy, long-handled
Paraguayan type, and shovels have been similarly generalized
to the long, square-bladed form in common use throughout
Paraguay. Rakes and forks are now used only rarely.

The persistent importance of hand-tools suggests that agriculture in La Colmena has not yet lost its pioneer flavor. Although
some colony lands have been farmed for more than 20 years,
the preparation of new land is a continuous process. In addition,
in later phases of settlement the Japanese penchant for clean
tillage has gradually been compromised, and in fields cluttered
with stumps, simple farming techniques remain the most
appropriate. Because Paraguayans do a significant amount of the
manual labor, acquisition of their tools was logical, and the
availability of Paraguayan implements facilitated acceptance.
In addition, the Paraguayan hoe has proved clearly superior to
traditional types in combating tough tropical weed growth and
in cultivating new land. The machete has been universally
adopted on the strength of its obvious utility.[36] A hand-operated
seeder similar to those in use in most of the German colonies
is also common.[37]

In spite of the trend toward simplification and acceptance of
Paraguayan substitutes, Japanese colonists have preserved a
few specialized implements that involve specific tasks or require particular techniques. The kama (harvesting sickle) is in
general use, and Japanese-style saws remain common. The
threshing flail continues to be manufactured, and wheat growers
still prefer to thresh by beating bundles against a raised, slotted
wooden platform. Shell-shaped winnowing baskets are fashioned
of split bamboo by one colonist, who is largely responsible for
preserving this and other Japanese forms of basketry.

Animal-drawn implements of the light "walking" variety,
including steel plows, harrows, weeders, cultivators, and spike
rakes were introduced. Most Japanese own one or more of these
and use them when circumstances permit. Among a few colonists
the preference for horsepower and concomitant harnessing techniques is still evident, particularly when light tasks such as
discing are involved. However, the majority of settlers use

pairs of horn-yoked oxen, probably because plowing is relegated to peons whenever possible.

c. Farming techniques: In the organization of their cultivated areas, pioneers have preserved much of their characteristic sense of order. Forest is cleared to produce a single rectilinear planting area. Cultivated land is subdivided into smaller rectangular units to facilitate rotation, and individual fields are defined by linear mounds of earth that are often planted to thatch, forage, or other useful plants. Field crops occupy neat rows aligned with nearly mathematical precision, and spaces between them are usually free of weeds.

Colonists have readily subsituted the prevailing metric system for their own units of areal measurement. The hectare and the cho correspond closely in size (2.47 vs 2.45 acres) and from the beginning were used interchangeably. Farmers still occasionally refer to smaller parcels of land according to the number of tan, particularly in connection with rice cultivation,38 but land measures are seldom expressed in Japanese units, and hectares are used in all records kept by the colony cooperative.

Most cultivated land in the colony is not fenced. Because Paraguayans are not accustomed to pen livestock, protection for plantings has always been necessary. Unfortunately, most colonists remain financially unable to provide adequate barriers against foraging cattle, and in a number of colony-wide meetings, no group solution to the problem has been found. The cooperative has managed to erect some barbed wire fences on colony borders and to place gates at bridges and other critical points. Colonists themselves employ various expedients, including the simple Paraguayan fence, or they fashion more effective living barriers by bending double the branches of thorny young apepú trees and interweaving them. As yet, however, fencing is not a significant component of the landscape.

In the actual processes of tillage, the annual march of the seasons provides only broad and ill-defined controls. For the Japanese, who are accustomed to rely upon seasonal changes and their indicators as specific cues to a wide range of behavior, the lack of seasonal imperatives has required considerable adjustment. The agricultural calendar is highly flexible, and regardless of experience, the element of speculative risk is difficult to escape. Planting and harvesting times extend over several months (Table 10), and there are no reliable natural indicators

TABLE 10

Planting and Harvesting Times of Principal Crops

Crop	Planting Time	Optimum	Harvest Time
Mandioca	June – Nov.	July – Sept.	May
Cotton	Sept. – Dec.	Oct.	Mar. – Apr.
Maize	June – Dec.	July – Sept.	Dec. – May
Rice	Oct. – Jan.	Nov.	Apr. – May
Beans	Sept. – Mar.	Oct. – Dec.	May – June
Onions	Mar. – Apr.	. . .	Sept. – Nov.
Wheat	June – Aug.	. . .	Oct.
Potatoes	June – Aug.	. . .	Sept. – Nov.
Peanuts	Sept. – Feb.	Sept. – Oct.	May
Tobacco	May – June	. . .	Feb. – Mar.

Source: Consensus of informants.

to aid selection. As a result, there is little or no seasonal concentration of effort, and conscientious farmers are constantly
occupied.

Additional pressures result from the fact that the growing
season usually accommodates two crops. Double-cropping was
introduced in the first years of settlement; however, poorly
adapted seed varieties and lack of familiarity with local conditions militated against early experiments, and the practice did
not become general until the early 1950's. Onions, potatoes, and
wheat are "winter" crops and precede cotton, maize, beans, or
soybeans. To fit two crops into the agricultural year, it is often
necessary to plant the second crop before the first is harvested.

Although individual crops require some variations in technique, all colonists manifest a similar approach to the mechanics
of cultivation. All colonists are not equally skilled, and farming
operations are influenced to some extent by size of holdings; but
methods of clearing, planting, weeding, harvesting, and threshing,
as well as elements of conservation and crop defense, are fairly
standardized.

With the exception of rice cultivation, all lands intended for
farming must be cleared of imposing subtropical forest. In the
first decade, colonists cleared their own land, but most of them
now hire Paraguayans. Few farmers clear every year, but an
average of one-half acre of new land per settler is incorporated
annually into the colony's total cultivated area. Clearing involves

felling of trees and occasional girdling of the largest specimens. Some colonists permit Paraguayan laborers to leave palms standing, but most farmers insist upon their removal. Woody growth is burned when it is dry. Before planting, branches are sawed from trunks, piled around stumps and logs, and burned a second time. Larger trunks must be burned for several years, and hoe culture must be practiced until most of the debris is removed. In early clearing the Japanese removed stumps so that they could employ their animal-drawn machinery. However, the practice has been abandoned, and in newer fields stumps are occasionally reburned or left to rot.

In fields relatively free of debris, land is prepared for planting with iron mold-board plows. Three plowings are usually necessary, and discing or raking occasionally precedes the opening of furrows. Planting procedures depend upon the crop. Onions, rice, tobacco, and various vegetables are planted in viveros in spite of the additional labor and expense. Farmers plant other field crops with hand seeders or simply drop the crops in furrows and cover them with soil, using a hoe or the foot. Maize and beans are planted in the same field but at different intervals so that mature maize stalks can be used to support vines.

Fields are commonly weeded at regular intervals. Some fields are kept scrupulously clean, but farmers obviously are becoming less concerned with the matter. Whether the change is the result of conscious recognition of the effect of direct sunlight and the elements upon soil microbiology and structure, or simply part of the general trend toward carelessness in agriculture, could not be determined. Weeding is accomplished by hoeing rather than by cultivation, because disturbing the surface soil increases the possibility of water loss by evaporation.

Harvesting is accomplished entirely by hand. Labor is occasionally massed for harvesting cotton, wheat, and rice because of possible damage from the unpredictable weather. The same sense of urgency is not always attached to other crops. Maize and beans may be left in the fields and picked in small amounts when labor is available or when the market dictates. Grains and beans are threshed on the farm. Cotton is spread for drying on long raised bamboo platforms. No other forms of processing are normally associated with farm activity.

Paraguayans are employed in almost all tasks related to

agriculture, and they do the bulk of the clearing, plowing, and weeding.[39] Nevertheless, farmers have shown some reluctance to completely surrender certain tasks to Paraguayans. Some Japanese still prefer to do their own planting. Preparation of viveros and transplanting are invariably done by colonists, and surplus seedlings are often planted along roads or in other normally wasted areas (Figure 38). Harvesting may be done by Paraguayans, but Japanese usually work along with them to give supervision. Threshing is almost always reserved for family or cooperative labor, and groups of Japanese circling piles of beans or grain while they apply their articulated bamboo flails are still a common sight.

Paddies are cultivated more or less according to custom. It has been difficult to accustom Paraguayans to work in the paddies, and much of the labor is still done by Japanese. Raised benches along streams consist of poorly drained land to which water seldom needs to be brought. Benches are subdivided into small, interconnected diked fields designed to utilize and eventually

FIGURE 38

K. Miamoto, preparing seedbeds for a variety of garden vegetables (including lettuce, in foreground). In background is cotton planted on land cleared three years before. Note forest debris, including smoldering stump. Sr. Miamoto is holding a Japanese-style saw, as well as a Paraguayan-type axe.

drain away surplus water. Fields are plowed when dry, then flooded and worked to proper planting consistency. Seedlings are planted by hand and spaced by means of knotted string. Plantings are staggered in order to extend the harvest over several months. Paddies are weeded twice, then drained before harvest.

Perennial plantings follow the general pattern established in the German colonies of central Paraguay. Seeds are first planted and carefully tended in viveros, and seedlings are transferred to fields after nine months to one year. Further care is restricted to weeding, except for grapes. Grapes are planted according to the so-called Italian system in which wires elevated by posts support rows of plants. Pruning must be done annually.

Pioneer farmers are aware of most basic conservation techniques and are kept continually conscious of their value by the colony cooperative and other organizations noted elsewhere. Unfortunately, colonists have been unable to cultivate on a basis that would assure sustained yields. Simple measures, such as contour plowing, are usually practiced where necessary, but more complicated, time-consuming, or expensive techniques receive little emphasis. As a result of careless "pillage agriculture," as the Japanese themselves have termed it, yields throughout the colony have steadily declined, and regular clearing of new land has become an economic necessity.

Colonists recognize the value of fertilizers, but their failure to apply them represents one of the more drastic departures from traditional practice. Paddies and viveros occasionally receive locally available materials, including cottonseed, bone meal, and animal wastes. However, most cultivated land has never been fertilized. Because few farmers keep many animals the supply of manure is limited, and human wastes are never gathered. Plant refuse is seldom conserved. Commercial fertilizers must be imported and hence are prohibitively expensive. Japanese rationalize the sacrifice of such an obviously beneficial technique as an inevitable consequence of the size of their operations and unfavorable returns from the agricultural economy. However, as yields have progressively declined, their disadvantage grows, and the cheaper process of clearing new land is considered the only recourse.[40]

Crop rotation as a method of preserving soil fertility is widely understood. However, only since 1950 has the practice become common. In the first years, cotton provided the only reliable source of income, and economic pressures forced colonists to devote all available land to its production. By 1950, declining yields, the appearance of root fungus, the vagaries of the cotton market, and the consequent trends toward polyculture and double-cropping all contributed to the establishment of rotation as a basic technique.

There is no standard formula for rotation. The normal progression of "summer" and "winter" crops restricts choice, but beans or other legumes are included every other year or so, and these are plowed under when farmers feel they can spare the expected return. Many informants claimed to practice specific systems. However, schedules are extremely flexible, and farmers react more readily to the market than to rigid programs. Totally exhausted fields are occasionally planted to beans for three or more years, or fallowed, or planted in pasture.

Declining yields have also resulted from improper seed selection. Failure of imported seed varieties of all crops has been common, and still occurs. Farmers are conscious of the need for selection, but the practice is informal and rudimentary.

Crop defense, according to most informants, requires little attention. Except for occasional incursions of locusts and leaf-cutting ants, insect pests are not a cause of major concern. Pests associated with specific crops, such as the maize borer, tobacco mosaic, phylloxera (which attacks grapes, etc.), are controlled by sprays acquired through the cooperative. Root rot in cotton poses a more difficult problem and at the moment can be combated only by rotation. In addition, cotton plants are uprooted and burned after each harvest.

Current agricultural practice among La Colmena colonists is obviously the resultant vector between the forces of tradition and those of experience. Evidently, colonists have not entirely discarded attitudes conditioned by the traditional Japanese "small land" and "pressure production" psychology. Yet the commitment to large holdings in near-tropical latitudes has placed severe strains upon a system fundamentally geared to intensive tillage of small units. Since the role of experience in shaping resultant compromises has been profound, it is necessary to account for factors that have influenced its course.

Planners responsible for La Colmena were clearly aware that traditional Japanese farming methods were not necessarily applicable to tropical and subtropical pioneering. However, in their haste to establish a Paraguayan colony before changes could occur in the prevailing political climate, the Japanese were unable to learn much about local agricultural conditions. Under the circumstances, it is not surprising that the attempt was made to draw upon colonization experience from Brazil; the original survey team and colony administrators came from Brazil, and 12 families with pioneering experience in São Paulo were settled in various zones of the new colony to serve as advisors and models.

It has been pointed out elsewhere that the attempt to apply Brazilian agricultural experience to Paraguayan ecological conditions was nearly disastrous. Apparently few of the pioneers brought from Brazil were farmers by trade. More serious difficulties evolved from the assumption that Paraguayan climatic conditions were identical with those of the settlement frontier in São Paulo. The unsuccessful attempts to establish upland rice have been noted, but the direct transfer of Brazilian agricultural timing for all major crops resulted in additional failures.

The remarkable patience exhibited by colonists in the face of persistent mismanagement and faulty advice was no doubt based upon a strong sense of discipline and was reinforced by the artificial cohesion resulting from isolation. Perhaps, too, the administration was able to capitalize upon the malleability of a large number of pioneers who had no previous farming experience. Eventually, however, farmers began to disengage themselves from the administration.

Unfortunately, the reservoir of agricultural skills was neither large nor uniform, and many colonists were fortified with little more than their own powers of observation and willingness to experiment. Although nationalistic feeling engendered by the war strengthened colony unity, farmers turned increasingly to guidelines provided by personal experience hard won through trial and error. Variations from farm to farm in details of cultivation indicate that colonists are still inclined to seek independent solutions to individual problems.

How and by whom individual pioneer experience has been shaped is not entirely clear. The basic character of farming was early circumscribed by the company in terms of the crops and tools chosen for emphasis, but as a result of failure, methods imported from Brazil were discredited. The influence of Paraguayans seems to have been minimal. The Paraguayan government offered instruction in agronomy to entering colonists, but informants are unanimous in classifying the experience as useless.

Paraguayan residents in La Colmena have afforded ample opportunity for advice or example. Relatively reliable general information has been acquired concerning planting times and perhaps other minor matters, but Paraguayans are not ordinarily considered a valid source of information. The Paraguayan is freely employed as a unit of energy when the task is simple, and he is usually left to use his own tools and methods. But the colonist is clearly conscious of the divergence in goals and attitudes that distinguishes him from his less sophisticated native neighbor. Pioneer farming is industrious, technological, and commercial. Colonists feel that they have little to learn from those whose system of cultivation is relaxed and undisciplined, motivated by the simple satisfaction of elemental current needs and surrounded with an aura of mystical superstition.

It is worth noting that the extensive body of Paraguayan agricultural folklore has had little influence upon Japanese behavior. Reacting against pioneer methods, which they felt to be irrationally destructive, Paraguayans attempted to "rescue" colonists by imparting to them some of their own current weather- and farming-lore. The heavy infusion of Christian religion reduced possibilities for acceptance, but the Japanese proved skeptical on more than religious grounds. Colonists from urban backgrounds have been expectably agnostic about such matters, but those who were farmers also generally dismiss beliefs as baseless superstitions, and second-generation adults usually agree.[41] The few farmers who are disposed to experiment with Paraguayan lore show a predictable ambivalence: For most crops, folk prescriptions are possible sources of useful information, but in rice cultivation the Parguayans have nothing to teach the Japanese.

Although pioneers are inclined to place primary value on individual experiment, they remain guardedly open-minded to new opportunities. Colonists continue to view agriculture as a technological problem, and, in spite of residual distrust of colony-wide organizations, they have created several institutions to seek solutions. The economic role of the colony cooperative is discussed below, but important secondary functions include study, experiment, and advice, and distribution of new seed, fertilizer, and machinery. A recently established cultural organization also acquires and disseminates useful new agricultural information. As yet, however, there is no colony-run experi-

mental farm, and acceptance of advice from organizations is
still far from universal.

d. The agricultural economy: Japanese colonists grow almost
exclusively to sell. A small amount of edible produce is retained,
and both kitchen gardens and small paddies are intended solely
for food supply. However, the Japanese are not required by
festival, religious, or social-exchange obligations to conserve
a portion of their crops, and as there are no cottage industries
based upon agricultural raw materials, almost all produce is
sold off the farm immediately after harvest.

Most colonists market crops through some form of collective
organization. Because these organizations have constructed
storage facilities in the town of La Colmena, colonists have not
been required to store their harvests for long periods, and
barns or other storage devices, though occasionally present, are
not conspicuous in the rural landscape.

Location of marketing mechanisms within the colony has also
affected patterns of transport. Colonists have for the most part
been spared the arduous and time-consuming journeys by oxcart
to urban markets, and development of individual transport capability has received little emphasis. The Japanese brought a few
bicycles and handcarts, but these have been discarded. Most
Japanese possess a horse or two and several colonists have built
small sleds for moving tools, seed, and fertilizer around the farm.
Although bulk transport moves over colony roads in ox-drawn
carretas, few colonists own one because they can be easily leased
or borrowed in the event that they are not supplied by the purchaser
of the harvest.

From 1936 until 1943, the administration representing the
Paraguay Colonial Bureau seems to have been an unavoidable
link in the chain between farmer and market. The actual economic
functions of the company are not clear, and many informants
claim that from the beginning they were free to market their
products as they chose. The scanty evidence is contradictory,
but it is unlikely that the company manipulated production yet
remained disinterested in marketing.

Although the war reduced the influence of the company, the
production from pioneer agriculture was sufficient to induce
several entrepreneurs from Asunción to establish branches in
La Colmena. With the establishment of a cooperative in 1948
the activities of these firms were curtailed. But in spite of

difficult competition two firms remain, continuing to handle a modest percentage of the colony's production.

Since its founding in July 1948, the Agricultural Cooperative Union—No-Kyo-Kumiai, Cooperativa La Colmena, Sociedad Rural Limitada (SRL)—has slowly emerged as the dominant force in the management of colony agriculture. The need for such an organization has never been unanimously felt. It is indicative of lingering suspicions and a well-developed sense of independence that less than half of the colonists agreed to subscribe the initial quotas. As yet the cooperative has failed to integrate the production of the entire colony. Membership still does not include all Japanese farmers, but it has steadily increased from 50 Japanese to 80 (about 80 percent of the total number of heads of farm families). From the inception of the organization, Paraguayan farmers owning land in the colony were invited to join. Paraguayan membership fluctuates from year to year, but in 1958, 20 Paraguayans were enrolled. Although Paraguayans account for 20 percent of the membership, they actually farm less than 10 percent of the cultivated land registered to members.

The principal function of the cooperative is to dispose of the agricultural produce of its members. In performing this service, the organization has been forced to expand its activities. The cooperative owns a truck, has built storage facilities in Acahay and Ybytymí as well as in the colony, and has opened a retail outlet in Asunción. The organization has also been forced to maintain the road between La Colmena and Acahay and to operate several basic agricultural industries to complement the crop complex.

Members are required to market "obligatory" crops (cotton, maize, beans, peanuts) through the cooperative, for which a small commission is charged. Tung and grapes must also be sold through the cooperative. "Optional" crops (onions, potatoes, tobacco, and rice) may be sold on the open market. However, all sales must be reported to the cooperative, and profits are added to the sum upon which fees and assessments are calculated.

An integral part of the cooperative's involvement in production includes improvement of yields through conservation, introduction of new crops, and operation of agricultural industries. At the moment, the conservation program is limited mainly to propaganda, although imported seed varieties, fertilizers, and tools are sold through the cooperative's retail outlet. In the search for new sources of farm income, the organization's chief contribution has been the introduction of grape production. Techniques of viticulture and wine-making were borrowed from the highly successful German vintners of Colonia Independencia, and the colony currently produces several thousand gallons of wine annually. Other projects are under consideration, including the planting of grapefruit and revival of the petitgrain industry.

Although the cooperative has undeniably improved the lot of most colonists, the pooling of productive energies alone has failed to resolve many serious problems. The agricultural union, with fewer than 100 members, is far too small to function effectively. It cannot control sufficient produce to acquire bargaining advantage in the Paraguayan market. Nor can the cooperative mobilize sufficient capital to supply much-needed agricultural and industrial equipment or to provide funds for experiment, conservation, fencing, seed, and road maintenance. With so few members, it is impossible to implement plans for expansion and further diversification of agriculture, which colonists feel to be the most certain means to ultimate prosperity.

Many problems facing Japanese pioneers are beyond the scope of the agricultural union. The cooperative has been unable, for example, to protect colonists from the profit-squeeze that affects all producers in Paraguay. Prices received for agricultural commodities are prohibitively low when compared with the cost of imported fertilizers, seed, implements, and other prerequisites of stable productive agriculture. Even with collective effort, the Japanese have little hope of purchasing the mechanized equipment required to revive worn-out fields by deep plowing—a practice necessary not only to tap nutrient resources of subsoils but also to destroy clay hardpans that have apparently formed as the result of decades of continuous cultivation coupled with clean tillage.

The cooperative has also been unable to compensate for the lack of active interest in, or concerted effort toward, improvement of the colony on the part of the Paraguayan government. La Colmena, along with other colonies, has suffered the effects of turbulent Paraguayan politics. The cooperative has attempted, without notable success, to assume some of the burdens normally shouldered by the government. The vital road to Acahay has been kept open, but deterioration is outrunning meager resources for maintenance. Farm credit is available only from private sources.[42]

Obviously, many problems affecting agricultural economics cannot be handled with the resources available to colonists. But there are indications that help will be forthcoming. In 1957, diplomatic relations at the ambassadorial level were re-established between Paraguay and Japan, and after a lapse of 15 years colonists were given direct contact with official representatives of the home government. Colony leaders immediately presented their problems and in 1958 received a low-interest loan of approximately $30,000 to bolster the cooperative. Plans for new Japanese immigration call for economic guarantees, including direct linkage of new settlements with foreign and particularly Japanese markets. It is possible though by no means certain that such projects will benefit La Colmena.

Industry and Commerce

Industry in La Colmena is on a small scale and almost entirely concerned with processing local agricultural produce. As with all other livelihood activities in the colony, Japanese have assumed the dominant role; furthermore, most colony industry is managed by the Agricultural Cooperative Union.

The original colonization company seems to have recognized the relation between processing and profit in Paraguay and has established several industries based upon local resources, including a sawmill, a brick factory, a cotton gin, a rice mill, a wheat-flour mill, a pork-processing plant, and a machine shop for repair of agricultural implements. Of these, only the cotton gin and the rice mill proved useful to colonists, but they were established with antiquated equipment and, with all other industries, were abandoned during the war.

In 1949 the cooperative bought all industrial enterprises from the defunct company but has been able to re-equip only the cotton gin and the rice mill. These two plants, along with the small winery established with the help of the Japanese government, comprise all industry of practical consequence. One colonist, with the help of entrepreneurs in Asunción, has established a small winery and has acquired a motorized grain thresher, and two Paraguayans operate a primitive brick-and-tile factory. However, the output of noncooperative industry is inconsequential. Total employment for all industries, which are located in or near the planta urbana, does not exceed 100. Work is highly seasonal, particularly at the winery where the entire year's operation is compressed into two months.

The importance of industry to the colony's economy is widely recognized. Almost all agricultural commodities must be processed in some way before entering into commerce. The processor, or elaborator, not only requires a share of the profit but also controls prices paid to producers. In La Colmena, the Japanese have found it advantageous to create their own processing facilities, and all plans for the future consider processing an integral part of any agricultural enterprise.

Cottage industries are of little significance. Among the Japanese a carpenter and a basket maker ply their crafts when opportunity permits, but the patterns of off-season or women's employments that are characteristic in rural Japan do not obtain in La Colmena. In town several Paraguayans make saddlery or furniture, and farmers prefer to purchase them rather than fashion such items themselves.

In retail commerce the Japanese exert an influence out of proportion to their numbers. The agricultural union maintains the largest retail outlet, which provides the community with a wide variety of household and dry goods. In spite of difficulty in agriculture, which usually signals a wholesale rush by pioneers into the establishment of boliches, only three Japanese have become merchants.[43] Yet, next to the cooperative, their stores are the largest and most frequently patronized by both colonists and native Paraguayans.

Other Livelihood Activities

The Japanese currently engage in little or no productive activity that is not directly related to agriculture, and even in the settlement's initial stages, farming consumed nearly all the colonists' time and energy. Lumbering, which has helped many a colonist, or colony, over early difficulties, was never important in La

Colmena. The most accessible timber was logged off prior to sale of the land. The colonization company established a sawmill to process the little that remained, but few settlers bothered to bring their logs to the planta urbana.

Hunting and gathering were a necessary part of the food quest during the first few years when the production of food fell short of requirements. According to informants, grasses and fungi were regularly gathered, and as this activity was common in Japan the colonists preferred to use their own judgment on the question of edibility rather than consult Paraguayans. Today these practices have been abandoned, and hunting has been reduced to the role of a sport practiced by a very small minority. Animals taken alive are usually kept as pets, as are birds and fish, but only those colonists living in town have time to devote to such matters.

Of all nonagricultural activities only fishing has managed to generate a continuous and organized interest. When larders empty of fish, colonists press the cooperative truck into service for a combined outing and fishing expedition to the Tebicuary River, 80 miles to the southwest. Several tons of fish are caught with nets and transported to the colony for salting. Expeditions follow no particular pattern but are held three or four times a year when the need arises. Needless to say, Paraguayans take a dim view of organized depredations upon this native resource, even though fishing has little direct meaning in native subsistence patterns.

ADDITIONAL CULTURAL FACTORS
IN MAN - LAND RELATIONSHIPS

In the morphology of any cultural landscape, not all facets of culture weigh equally, and for some traits the connections with terrestrial phenomena are tenuous. However, to interpret the cultural geography of Japanese settlement in La Colmena it is necessary to enlarge perspectives beyond simple and direct man - land relationships. The following discussion of essentially nonmaterial culture traits lacks the statistical precision that signifies validity to the sociologist. In addition, the selection and treatment of behavioral elements is certain to displease anthropologists as well as most geographers—anthropologists on the grounds of an increasing reluctance to fragment culture, geographers on questions of relevance. The lack of statistical evidence is regretted, and the choices are admittedly arbitrary. However, my intent is merely to indicate some of the more important factors, which, although occasionally reflected directly in land use, are integrally related to processes of cultural geographic change.

Diet

Until relatively recently, immigrant pioneers have resisted changes in their food habits, the basic staples of which conformed more or less to simplified rural Japanese patterns. Rice, noodles made from wheat flour, and numerous vegetables formed the basis of the pioneer diet. Sweet potatoes and soybeans, which are also consumed by Paraguayans, were included as secondary elements. A few minor items oriented to the preparation of specific dishes—adzuki, daikon—were also introduced. Animal protein was supplied by the products of fishing, and both eggs and poultry were eaten when available.

Among contrasting Paraguayan food habits, only the consumption of large quantities of fruit seems to have enjoyed rapid and general acceptance. During the first years of settlement, citrus fruit and bananas were planted around pioneer homesites, and fruit assumed a significant role in the diet as soon as trees began to bear. Out of curiosity, and occasionally necessity, colonists experimented with other Paraguayan foods, but when the colony's economy became stabilized, the Japanese almost invariably returned to their traditional staples.

A few conservative families still have not materially changed their eating habits. But by 1950 Paraguayan foods began to appear regularly on many tables, and by 1958 Paraguayan staples were at least as important as traditional ones in the general pioneer diet. Consumption of beef and pork increased markedly, although few colonists raised the necessary animals. Maize, mandioca, and beans were slower to enter the food complex, but their consumption is now widespread. Cheese and lard appeal to an increasing number of Japanese, but their use is not yet general. Currently about 25 percent of the pioneer families eat

primarily Paraguayan foods, some 15 percent adhere to an
essentially Japanese diet, and the remainder partake of traditional and local elements more or less equally. All pioneers
continue to consume a far greater number and variety of vegetables than is common among native residents. For most colonists,
also, fish remains a significant source of protein.

Paraguayan foods entering the pioneer diet have been accompanied by some of their associated culinary techniques. Several
of the most typical Paraguayan preparations, especially those
made with maize (chipa, sopa paraguaya, locro) are uncommon,
but most other simple combinations and techniques are known
and used.[44] There is no evidence that acceptance of Paraguayan
foods and cooking extends to the complex of folk beliefs with
which Paraguayans surround such matters.[45]

Japanese methods of food preparation have disappeared more
rapidly than the traditional staples to which they are applied.
Rice is still often cooked in the time-consuming Japanese manner,
but only rarely does one encounter bean curd, soba (noodle soup),
adzuki, daikon, or the more familiar sukiyaki, osushi, fried rice,
and shoyu. There is a marked tendency to reserve these and
other typically Japanese dishes for special occasions, and their
preparation is losing ground in daily cooking experience.[46]

Patterns of beverage consumption have undergone more rapid
changes. Yerba maté almost immediately replaced green tea,
which it vaguely resembles in taste, and today yerba is widely
consumed in all common Paraguayan forms.[47] The early sub-
stitution of caña for traditional alcoholic beverages indicates
that in this area also, barriers to acceptance were relatively
fragile. Wine and Paraguayan beer were also readily adopted,
although the consumption of alcoholic beverages among colonists is very low, and intoxication, at least in public, is exceedingly rare. The fabrication of alcohol by individual farmers is
not practiced. Drinks served to visitors depend upon a variety
of factors: Special guests are offered imported tea if families
can afford it; friends are served yerba maté in cool weather
and a refresco made from orange-flavored syrup and water on
hot days. In the planta urbana, Japanese occasionally offer local
alcoholic drinks, but in the agricultural zone this is extremely
uncommon.

The gradual shift toward Paraguayan dietary habits seems
closely linked to several specific processes. Japanese staple foods
were within the range of Paraguayan agricultural ecology, and

colonists turned immediately and persistently to their production. However, many delicacies and most traditional condiments were unobtainable from the start, thereby introducing an element of simplicity to many Japanese dishes, and actually eliminating others. Even without traditional ingredients the preparation of many Japanese dishes is complicated and time-consuming, and in the process of pioneering the necessary investment of time and energy has not always been possible.

The association of Japanese colonists with Paraguayan foods has been close from the beginning. The Japanese have regularly grown most of the Paraguayan staples for sale or feed, and their acceptance in the diet has required no changes in patterns of cultivation. Food items, such as beef, that were not produced by colonists became readily and cheaply available from the increasing number of Paraguayans residing in the colony. From the beginning, also, the Japanese were thoroughly exposed to the preparation and consumption of Paraguayan foods; the hiring of Paraguayan kitchen help is not common, but colonists acquired considerable practical experience during emergencies (such as the failure of the mountain rice crop), in trips outside the colony, and in feeding hired laborers, who invariably refused Japanese food.

It is possible that the ultimate acceptance of simpler Paraguayan foods and culinary techniques is chiefly a response to pressures of pioneering upon almost any custom involving considerable amounts of time, energy, and skill. Colonists themselves tend to rationalize the increasing dependence upon native foods as essential to good health in the Paraguayan environment.

Spiritual Considerations

Pioneer religious backgrounds are diverse. Currently about 80 percent of the family heads are Buddhist, approximately 5 percent are Shinto, and the remainder are Christian. Undoubtedly these two Oriental faiths are intermingled, as they were in prewar Japan. Christians include both Catholics and Protestants. Several younger family heads have been converted to Catholicism in the colony. However, according to informants at least four families came to La Colmena from the region along the south Japan coast in which the Catholic tradition has been preserved since its introduction by the Portuguese in the 16th century. At least five families from Brazil are Protestant (evangelistas), having been converted before coming to Paraguay by an undetermined sect (or sects).

Although Japanese no longer engage in public demonstrations of faith, spiritual feelings have not always been so submerged. In 1937 pioneers brought a stone from the national Shinto shrine at Ise and incorporated it in the pedestal of a small monument erected in the planta urbana in commemoration of the founding of the colony. According to informants, the monument began to assume attributes of a venerated place when, during a particularly serious drought, prayed-for rain actually fell. In addition, several traditional festivals with religious or quasi-religious connotations were celebrated regularly, including holidays commemorating Mejei-setsu (the origin of Japan), Tencho-setsu (the Emperor's birthday), and the New Year.

The outbreak of World War II greatly intensified nationalistic feelings among colonists. Although only a small minority professed the militaristic "official" Shinto faith, the entire Japanese community experienced a concomitant rise in religious fervor. Meetings were held to collect money for the war effort, and on such occasions prayers were offered for victory and for the war dead. In 1942 Paraguay assumed control of the colony and prohibited meetings for any purpose, but religious and nationalistic feelings remained high.

The shock of Japan's surrender, which had repercussions in nearly all phases of pioneer culture, profoundly affected patterns of religious practice. Spiritual convictions were deeply shaken by defeat. Subsequently all public demonstrations of Oriental faith vanished, and the shrine veneration formerly attached to the founder's monument gradually disappeared. Along roads, in fields, or near dwellings there are no artifacts reflecting Oriental religious orientation, and no celebrations of Japanese origin currently survive.[48] Without shrines or festivals, Buddhist and Shinto colonists now lack not only a focus of community religious expression but also an important traditional center of social integration and interaction. In addition, because no Oriental priests have entered the colony, there are no mechanisms for formal instruction, ritual practice, or organized worship.

Detachment from formal religion is also evident at the family level. Major life crises are rarely if ever accompanied by traditional rituals.[49] Household shrines are present in approximately half the Buddhist or Shinto homes. Such shrines are extremely modest, and since regular family worship is no longer common, they receive little care or attention.

Although most traditional forms of organized religious expression have disappeared, the Japanese apparently retain some of the personal or inner-directed aspects of Oriental spiritual philosophy. In the realm of man - nature relationships in particular, colonists continue to reflect Oriental concepts. No beliefs attached to specific natural phenomena were encountered, and the lunar calendar, which in prewar rural Japan served as a key to nature lore, festival regulation, and agricultural folk practices, is nowhere in use. However, the general equation of tranquillity of spirit with harmony in environmental relationships has played an important role in the colony, and many informants credit the salvation of the settlement to such feelings. For founders of the colony, the discovery of the cone-like peak in the Cerro Apitaguá was considered a good omen, and it was promptly named "Fuji-san" (Figure 39). The presence of this peak, which is visible from much of the colony, fostered the illusion among settlers

FIGURE 39

Fuji-san. In foreground, the native mbocayá palm is being allowed to invade the cotton plantation of a Paraguayan landowner in La Colmena.

that the landscape of La Colmena was "just like Japan." Colonists state categorically that this feeling was indispensable in sustaining them during the first discouraging years. In addition, Japanese still view the entire complex of nature as benign. Informants seldom mention droughts or locusts, but often comment upon, and seem to derive considerable comfort from, colors in the sunset, tranquillity of the dawn, and so on.

The retreat from active religious involvement and the lack of tangible evidence of Oriental religious orientation are noted as stemming directly from the defeatism induced by the outcome of World War II. However, the reactions of colonists are consistent with religious conditions in prewar Japan. In the 1930's the spiritual life of the average Japanese does not seem to have been well organized, and official efforts to impose nationalistic Shinto beliefs upon a largely Buddhist peasantry further clouded the issue. Furthermore, the body of mystical folk-beliefs loosely incorporated into established or formal religions were characteristic primarily of the farming population. In rapidly growing urban centers such items as the lunar calendar and agricultural lore were already losing ground. The presence of a large urban contingent among colonists may account in part for the lack of religious concern.

For Christian colonists, the patterns of religious behavior developed somewhat differently. During World War II, ethnic ties were sufficient to generate a common sense of purpose, but in the defeat of Japan, Christians found no cause to compromise their faith, and the spiritual gulf has grown perceptibly.

In some ways the position of the small number of Brazilian Protestants is not unlike that of practitioners of Oriental religions. As adult converts, the evangelistas are not well instructed, and without clergy to bolster their faith, or a specific meeting place around which to concentrate it, there is a distinct possibility that it will disappear as present membership dissolves through death or departure. At the moment, however, their religion is actively practiced: Meals are blessed, Protestant feast days are observed, and the faithful gather on an occasional Sabbath for Bible readings at the home of one of their number.

Japanese Catholics, although possessing the social sanction and the material means to practice their faith, have found, spiritually, little common ground in La Colmena. A large church was constructed through the efforts and contributions of the

entire colony, and a priest visits the community to offer Mass on
important feast days. Japanese are divided from the Paraguayans not
only by language and customs but by the mystical superstition and
fanaticism of Paraguayan religious practice. Colonists have found
it difficult to accept the apparent contradictions in basic religious
dogma and actual moral practices in Paraguay. As a result most
Japanese Catholics remain in the background.

The future of religion as a source of cultural cohesion is
clouded. Spiritual leanings of Japanese children are extremely
mixed. Children of families professing Oriental faiths are
rarely indoctrinated in the home, and those from Protestant
households show little inclination toward the religion of their
parents. Furthermore, the environment in which youngsters
must mature is now overwhelmingly Paraguayan. In the colony
as a whole, natives outnumber Japanese by nearly four to one.
In the planta urbana the ratio of Paraguayans to Japanese is more
than ten to one, and in the school, which draws pupils from the entire district, the numerical disadvantage of Japanese children is
even greater. Children are constantly exposed to established
dogma as well as the obvious advantages of accepting it. As yet
the trend toward conversion is not clear-cut. A few Japanese
children have been baptized, but parents seldom voluntarily offer
preschool youngsters for instruction or baptism. Thus, most
children delay commitment well into adolescence. Those who
are strongly influenced by the social and moral code at home
find barriers to acceptance in the lack of sophistication in
Paraguayan Catholicism, and tend to remain aloof from all
formal religion.

Social Organization

1. CLASS STRUCTURE   Evidence suggests that not all colonists
entered La Colmena on an equal social footing and that at least
some Japanese forms of class consciousness were transferred
to the new settlement. A few colonists were obviously more
wealthy than the majority—a differential attributable to contrasts in the amount of land owned in Japan. In view of the
relation between landownership and status in prewar Japan,
it is probable that class distinctions became associated with
economic differences in the new colony. Within the company
administration, also, social contrasts stemming from differences

in occupation, training, family background, and relative position of authority seem to have been emphasized by administrators themselves.

If class distinctions based upon values and conditions in Japan were part of the initial social order, they have largely, if not entirely, disappeared. Not all colonists are equally prosperous, and the extent of their current wealth is roughly proportional to their economic resources when entering the colony. But, although class feelings may have influenced the tendency toward land accumulation, social prerequisites no longer are directly correlative with landownership. There is some deference to the most wealthy, but apparently no formal recognitions of caste have survived the homogenizing influence of agricultural pioneering.

2. THE FAMILY   Japanese pioneers have struggled constantly to preserve traditional patterns of family integrity and solidarity. Initially, colony leaders attempted to inhibit "fraternization" in order to conserve the characteristic elements of obligation, authority, and responsibility in established families, as well as to shield incipient families from the consequences of the informality with which Paraguayans tend to view such ties. Feelings against intermarriage have been particularly strong, and in spite of the problems of obtaining wives from abroad and of mate selection within a small group, mixed marriages have been few. Informants report eight formal unions between Japanese men and Paraguayan women, but no Japanese females have participated in mixed marriages. In 1959 only two Japanese-Paraguayan couples, with a total of six children, were actually living in the colony.

If colonists have managed to preserve racial integrity, they have been less successful in defending other aspects of traditional Japanese family relationships. The incorporation of the wife of the eldest son into the husband's family is still common, and the establishment of younger male siblings as independent branch families on their own land remains accepted practice. Some eldest sons have forfeited their succession to family head by leaving the colony or abandoning farming, and daughters-in-law as a rule are far less subservient to the husband's family elders than was common in prewar Japan. Within the nuclear family, bonds of affection and often of responsibility remain strong, but without constant and unanimous social pressure the

entire fabric of obligation and cooperation functions less effectively than in Japan.

The most profound change in family structure, and for the
current study the most significant, is the inversion of family
authority that has occurred within the last decade. In La Colmena
the younger generation, often Nisei (Japanese born in Paraguay),
has gradually assumed family leadership and control of the colony. As parents have grown older and less able to meet the
physical demands of pioneering, offspring have acquired a larger
role in plantation management. In part, as noted below, the emergence of the younger generation as a major cultural force is a
consequence of their role in communications. It was the defeat
of Japan in World War II, however, which catalyzed the process
of authority inversion by prompting general and conscious retreat from control on the part of the original pioneer generation.
Informants are agreed that, the the vacuum created by "loss of
pride" and "feelings of shame," the assumption of leadership by
the younger generation was logical, necessary, and actively
encouraged.

The significance of this change to patterns of cultural geography is difficult to evaluate. Clearly, second-generation
Japanese are increasingly involved in decisions affecting not
only individual families but also the entire Japanese element.
Because Nisei have no personal acquaintance with homeland
traditions, the possibilities for accelerating the process of
acculturation are obviously greater. As yet the younger generation has had little opportunity to translate its influence into
discernible indicators of the direction in which the colony is
to be led.

3. COLONY ADMINISTRATION   Until 1940 the colony was
administered by representatives of the Paraguay Colonial
Bureau at meetings with family heads. In 1940 the settlement
was divided into kumi (districts) and a colony-wide meeting was
held to elect kumicho (district heads). Presumably the kumicho
defended the interests of their constituents, and company representatives were more or less bound by majority decision in
matters pertaining to colony welfare. Unfortunately, the system
appears to have been too complex, and lines of communication
with homeland authority were long and undependable. In the
final analysis the colony administration provided most of the

initiative and used the settler organization as a means of directing the activities of the colonists.

During World War II and the Paraguayan Civil War of 1947, civil liberties were suspended. In 1948, however, colonists attempted to reconstitute self-government, and the elected kumicho met with remnants of company authority until the final closing of the Paraguayan Colonial Bureau office in 1952. From 1952 until 1957, the colony cooperative assumed the various roles of the defunct company.

In 1957 the entire Japanese element joined in the formation of La Colmena Bunka Kyokai (Japanese Cultural Organization), and this group, apparently headed by the elected kumicho as well as other colony leaders, currently shares administration with the cooperative. For purposes of representation the agricultural lands in the colony are now divided into 16 kumi, composed of five to twelve families each.[50] Kumi, in turn, are grouped in ku (four larger units), whose kucho (leaders) are chosen by vote from among the kumicho.

The exact functions and limits of authority of this rather elaborate organizational hierarchy are difficult to determine. Undoubtedly the Japanese were left to govern themselves in most matters before World War II. In 1944 La Colmena was incorporated into the Paraguayan geopolitical framework as a distrito, and as such it possesses a full complement of Paraguayan authorities, including a juéz de paz (the colony's principal authority). Furthermore, most residents within the borders of the former colony are Paraguayans. Under the circumstances, it is difficult to see just what remains for colonists to administer. Obviously Japanese organizations are viewed with official tolerance as long as they do not infringe upon legally constituted civil authority.

In economic affairs involving the Japanese themselves, the organization is free to function, and both the Cooperative and the Bunka Kyokai rely on the kumi for sanction. As a social device, the kumi is also useful in generating cohesion through colony-wide participation in meetings and elections and in providing a forum for the expression of collective opinion. Many of the traditional attributes of the kumi have, however, apparently disappeared. Its basic function—rotating responsibility in civic cooperation—has been seriously prejudiced,[51] and the organization is little more than a mechanism for the dissemination of useful information. The house of the kumicho is still identified

by a bangi (wooden gong) which, according to colonists, is to be
sounded in case of fire, robbery, or other calamity requiring
group action. But in view of the pattern of dispersed settlement,
this vestigial mark of authority, like the office it represents,
is largely symbolic.

4. OTHER ORGANIZATIONS   The Agricultural Union, the
kumi, and the Bunka Kyokai have social as well as economic and
pseudo-political functions. All serve as means by which the
Japanese element in the colony is unified toward certain specific
ends. However, only the Bunka Kyokai, which, unlike the cooperative, is exclusively Japanese and embodies the membership of
the entire Japanese community, was established as an instrument
to renew contact with Japan and to foment collective reaction to
all colony-wide problems. As the organization was only founded
in 1957, it is too early to measure its role in colony affairs.
Its principal aims, including accumulation and dissemination of
agricultural information and interest in conditions of roads, are
indicative of the organization's general character. The Bunka
Kyokai is obviously designed to serve primarily as a major
force in practical matters of pioneer welfare and secondarily
as a way of keeping viable the connections with Japan.

Colony youth has been organized since 1954 into young men's
and women's clubs. At the moment, both groups concentrate
upon social and recreational matters. The Young Men's Club
has absorbed an athletic union founded in 1946 and cooperates
with its female counterpart in organizing games, dances, and
Japanese participation in the May 14-15 fiesta. Recently, the
youth groups have expanded their interests to include a wide
range of philanthropic, civic, and other activities. In addition,
the men's group has taken considerable initiative in maintaining
cultural identity. The club sponsors Japanese language classes,
intends to establish a library and to subscribe to Japanese
publications, and has initiated such typically Japanese recreations
as Sumo wrestling and shogi chess.

Another organization is worthy of mention although it no
longer exists in its original form, and, during its brief history,
it did not directly concern La Colmena. In 1953 a small group
of colony leaders met to consider ways to reopen the question
of Japanese immigration to Paraguay. The resultant organization, Compañía Nipo-Paraguayo de Colonización,[3] was largely
responsible for the establishment of several thousand Japanese

in Colonia Chávez. By reawakening Japanese interest in Paraguay, this organization, which has since been absorbed into Japanese official emigration machinery, also benefited the original colony. Regular contact with Japan was re-established, the plight of La Colmena settlers was brought to official attention, and some of the original pioneers were employed to advise on new colonization efforts. The increment of new immigrants bolstered Japanese spirits and influence, and several new families were induced to settle in La Colmena itself.[52]

All formal Japanese organizations have been formed relatively recently and none have yet matured into effective institutions; functions overlap, and accomplishment lags far behind intent. Furthermore, as a distinct minority the Japanese can no longer hope to press the entire colony into their own social mold, and even among themselves, divisive forces remain. Nevertheless, these organizations represent a conscious effort to re-establish unity and to salvage basic values that do not directly conflict with current circumstances.

5. RECREATION   Among Japanese colonists, organized recreation has important social overtones. With the disappearance of Japanese festivals, various types of recreation, particularly athletics, have become the principal vehicle for general informal social intercourse. Sporting events are a basic feature of all holidays observed in the colony, and a day in August is specifically reserved for colony-wide competitions. Events are carefully planned, and formal institutions have been created specifically to construct facilities and to direct athletic activities. Through the efforts of Japanese youth groups, club houses and playing fields have been built in the planta urbana and the agricultural zone.

The association of athletics and social activity has been fostered in part by the nearly total lack of cross-cultural correspondence in patterns of recreation. Because of the Japanese choice of games and sports, Paraguayans rarely participate in them. The Japanese, on the other hand, show little inclination for soccer, and even less for horse-oriented forms of competition. Thus, colonists are free to incorporate athletics into their own distinctive social framework.

Athletic events usually emphasize track and field, with a particular emphasis on baseball. In transferring their predilection for

baseball to La Colmena, the Japanese have provided a rather
unique contribution to the Paraguayan landscape. The principal
diamond, constructed in the planta urbana in 1946, has accom-
modated as many as eight complete teams recruited from approximately 130 pioneer families. Teams are organized on a regional
basis, and although the Japanese community can now support
only three teams, the colony championship, decided each year
during the Independence - Founder's Day fiesta, still attracts
many enthusiastic colonists. Continued survival of the sport
presents a problem because it requires paraphernalia not
available in Paraguay. Interest has also gradually declined as
teams have been dissolved by departures, advancing age, or
other factors.

In some respects, the role of athletics as a medium combining
the attributes of recreation, celebration, and social intercourse
reflects the nearly complete absence of other forms of relaxation. There are no movies, and colonists do not frequent the
few small cantinas that are the colony's only regular source of
diversion. Weddings and similar occasions provide excuses for
small gatherings that are usually graced with the provision of
food and drink, but most colony-wide functions are organized by
Paraguayans, and Japanese seldom participate. On civic occasions, such as school graduations, a few representatives of the
Japanese community attend, but at dances and similar functions
they are conspicuous by their absence.

Thus, on either formal or informal levels, recreation provides
little opportunity for mixing native and immigrant elements.
There is no evidence that separation is intentional; indeed, polite
invitations are extended by both groups when colony-wide events
are contemplated. Colonists claim that agricultural pioneering
leaves little time for nonproductive pastimes. It is apparent,
however, that as a rule Japanese have not yet learned to derive
satisfaction from Paraguayan forms of relaxation. Paraguayans,
on the other hand, obviously continue to distinguish Japanese
from familiar elements related to their own culture. The peón -
patrón relationship, which most Paraguayan peasants in the
settlement have experienced, tends to interfere with free social
intercourse. But ethnic and perhaps racial barriers have not
entirely disappeared. Most colonists, including a majority of
the Nisei, do not feel "comfortable" at Paraguayan functions and
tend to avoid them.

6. SCHOOLS   In the first year of settlement, the Japanese constructed a school to formalize the instruction of colony youth. Because the school was intended to serve both natives and immigrants, it was patterned after Paraguayan models, employed a Paraguayan teacher, and in due course was officially incorporated into the national educational system. Although immigrant children were compelled to attend this Paraguayan school, colonists established a parallel system based upon Japanese methods in order to bridge the gap between local and accustomed standards, and to secure for their offspring the competitive advantage, either in Paraguay or Japan, of a high-caliber education. There can be little doubt that colonists also viewed their own school as an instrument for reinforcing cultural consciousness among Nisei.

In 1937 a teacher from Japan opened the first school devoted wholly to the teaching of the Japanese language, history, geography, and culture, and practical subjects such as mathematics. However, although settlers managed at one time to maintain three separate Japanese schools, the task of providing formal Japanese education proved exceedingly difficult. Japanese schools were not officially approved by the Paraguayan government, and during World War II, pressures were applied to close schools operated by immigrants from Axis countries. The Japanese continued instruction informally and clandestinely in private homes, but continuity and quality were difficult to maintain. At the war's end a number of colonists emigrated to other countries, leaving the burden of support for private schools on those who remained. The residue of permanent colonists struggled to sustain the entire system, but by 1952 only one school (the Yazawa Gakuen) remained open.

Japanese schools have also faced other problems. Not all colonists are now willing to support private educational institutions. Some parents feel that children of working age cannot be spared from the labor force and that the Paraguayan school is adequate. Several colonists also insist, for various reasons, that in their current circumstances the attempt to link the colony to Japan by any means, including schooling, is useless.

For students themselves, the difficulties inherent in the double system are enormous. Attendance at the Paraguayan school is compulsory, and little time is left for other instruction. The work load is not particularly heavy in either school, but when combined the total is awesome in relation to time available for study—an interval shortened considerably by the lack of adequate lighting and journeys up to several miles to the planta urbana.

The Yazawa Gakuen continues to function, although the institution still has not been officially sanctioned, and certificates of graduation are meaningless. At least 75 percent of the children born to Japanese parents have been exposed to some Japanese schooling, but not all these have completed the eight-year course. At the moment, approximately 30 student are enrolled. Japanese children attend the Yazawa Gakuen for two years before entering the Paraguayan primary school. Formerly students attended the Paraguayan school in the morning and Japanese classes in the afternoon. In the opinion of parents the burden upon children proved too great, and the Yazawa Gakuen now offers instruction only during vacations. Instruction in either school goes only through the sixth year, and further education must be obtained outside the colony. Most colonists aspire to provide additional education for children, but the expense is prohibitive for many, and the average educational level remains low.

Currently the Japanese school is neither an effective educational device nor an effective medium for transmission of Japanese culture. Exposure to Japanese education tends to separate Japanese children from their Paraguayan neighbors and may even generate a certain amount of cultural consciousness. But the exposure is brief and occurs at an age when powers of absorption and discrimination are not well developed. Colonists admit, also, that the caliber of instruction is substandard. Textbooks from Japan are available, but no new teacher has entered the colony since World War II. Most subjects have been dropped from the curriculum, particularly those dealing with purely Japanese subject matter. The sole remaining function of the school is to teach reading and writing of the Japanese language. In the process, simple elements of Japanese folk music and lore are introduced, but these are neither systematized nor emphasized.

Language

Difficulty with native languages is a common experience for
immigrant pioneers, and La Colmena Japanese offer no exception.
A few administrators spoke Spanish, and families from Brazil,
with varying backgrounds in Portuguese, rapidly learned sufficient Spanish to conduct business and supervise labor. However,
for all other colonists the learning of totally unrelated languages
proved extremely difficult, and most of the original pioneers
continue to depend upon others in dealings with Paraguayans.

Children, on the other hand, have readily acquired both
Spanish and Guaraní in addition to Japanese. Spanish is taught
formally in the Paraguayan school, and Guaraní is absorbed
through informal associations with Paraguayans. Choice of
language by younger Japanese depends somewhat upon the circumstances. Youth club meetings are held in Japanese, and
with elders Japanese is also usually employed. The younger
generation is inclined to consciously exploit its trilingualism,
speaking Spanish or Guaraní within earshot of parents, and con-
versing in Japanese among Paraguayans.

As the Nisei element grows in proportion to the original immigrant generation, Spanish appears to be gradually displacing
Japanese as the principal pioneer language. However, the rate
of change seems considerably slower than the pace at which
Paraguayan languages have invaded other ethnic groups. The
Japanese emphasize their language as the basis of cultural
identity, and the Japanese school, imperfect as it is, contributes
to the viability of spoken Japanese. Unfortunately, schooling
provides a poor foundation in reading and writing skills, and
because the colony has always been too small to support a news-
paper or other form of publication, such skills have no regular
application.

In the home, spoken Japanese continues to play a significant
role. Parental attitudes vary, depending upon, among other
things, ability to comprehend Spanish; but in most homes visited,
children responded in Spanish to parents, and conversed among
themselves in Spanish without reaction from elders.

In La Colmena the relations between language and culture
change are both direct and indirect. As noted earlier, the lack
of ability to communicate has severely circumscribed the fre-

quency and circumstances of pioneer - native contact. Until
children became proficient in Spanish and Guaraní and sufficiently
adult to participate in management of farms, a period of from
four to seven years passed during which colonists and Paraguayans
were separated by a substantial linguistic barrier. Japanese were
loath to hire laborers with whom negotiation and supervision were
enormously difficult, and social contacts (even had the Japanese
viewed them as desirable) were effectively canceled as sources
of influence.

The language barrier also served to bind colonists firmly to
the colonization company; pioneers from Brazil assumed a major
role in planning and management, and the company administration
itself functioned as an unavoidable link in all relationships with
Paraguayans. As children grew in language proficiency, direct
contacts between pioneers and Paraguayans became more frequent.
In the process, settlers were exposed to an expanding range of
Paraguayan behavior, and the colonization company was gradually
superseded as arbiter of which native patterns were suitable for
transmission.

Perhaps more critical to the present problem is the association of language capability with the younger pioneer generation.
As young Japanese acquired the Paraguayan languages, their
position evolved from the status implied by traditional family
structure to that of full participating members of the community.
The outcome of World War II accelerated the inversion of authority in the family and in the management of the colony, but the
process may well have had its origin in the role of the younger
generation in communication. In any case, Nisei facility with the
Paraguayan languages has placed the burden of interpreting native
culture upon the segment of the community that is most sensitive
to pressures for assimilation.

Pioneer Values and Problems of Culture Contact

In rural Paraguayan culture, Japanese pioneers are presented
with a variety of established solutions to problems encountered
in attempting to function in an unfamiliar environment. To
qualify as acceptable, such solutions, as well as other native
traits, must be tested against a pre-existing set of standards.

The process of sorting new elements into acceptable vs non-acceptable behavior is in large part a function of the basic value structure that characterizes Japanese culture.

In the present work it is not possible to examine all themes or individual values that might possibly bear upon the problem of Japanese reactions to new circumstances, but it is necessary to acknowledge some aspects of pioneer values that have conditioned contact and influenced cultural interchange. It is essential, also, to isolate and examine changes in values which, by altering the relations between native and introduced cultures, are critical to the processes of change.

The most geographically cogent elements in pioneer value structure are closely associated with migration motives. These are complex and tend to be highly individual, but all colonists note "lack of opportunity" as a significant factor in the decision to leave Japan. Opportunity was construed largely in terms of economic self-betterment, with considerable emphasis upon the necessity for success and unpardonable loss of face in failure. However, the determinants of success have until recently remained largely unrelated to local contexts. Colonists preserve a sense of region and particularly family in Japan, as well as an awareness of Japanese pioneer ventures elsewhere and even now are inclined to equate their achievements with these rather than Paraguayan standards.[53]

Colonists continue to value indicators of success and status recognizable to Japanese, and much pioneer behavior related to land occupance seems to have been oriented accordingly. In contrast to the rather casual view of landownership among Paraguayans, Japanese are firmly attached to the principle. Land is an indispensable instrument of wealth accumulation through production. In La Colmena, where rapid accumulation of wealth has proved difficult, land is indeed the only concrete symbol of accomplishment, and acquisition does not necessarily bear a direct relation to realistic future expansion of production. Satisfaction is derived from ownership and the knowledge that obligations to offspring and branch families can be fulfilled generously. Surplus funds are occasionally lavished on dwellings, but material possessions have little meaning unless they are associated with the process of wealth accumulation through agriculture.[54]

The Japanese approach to agriculture, or, for that matter, to all resource exploitation, is severely pragmatic. As the only representatives of their race and culture in Paraguay until 1955, La Colmena colonists felt themselves under additional pressures to show significant results. Unfortunately, conditions in Paraguay militated against rapid or large returns from cultivation. As a result, colonists were forced to place increasingly heavy demands upon the land. Although cultivation practices have been tempered somewhat by a certain harmonious regard for nature and for the aesthetic pleasure derived from an orderly as well as productive landscape, the agricultural system has evolved in a ruthless and often irrationally exploitive way. Apparently colonists tend to view farming less as a way of life than as a mechanical process for the satisfaction of economic goals.

Labor and its role in goal achievement are closely associated with strong motivations for successful accomplishment. Unlike Paraguayans, colonists do not view manual labor as a mark of inferior status or as a necessary evil to be circumvented when possible. On the contrary, capacity for hard physical labor is a source of satisfaction and pride; it permits one to carry his share honorably in the community and is a valuable asset if not a prerequisite to success.

Japanese colonists apply themselves to hard physical labor with a single-minded constancy that bewilders Paraguayans. Pioneers have a well-developed sense of future that keeps goals firmly fixed, and activities not directly related to the achievement of those goals are likely to be considered superfluous. Because Japanese perceive their actions in an extended time context, goals themselves tend to be long-range; behavior is considered in terms of future consequences, plans are made that provide continuity of behavior over long periods of time, and delays or sacrifices are not necessarily fatal to projected activities. In La Colmena, interruptions are accepted relatively philosophically, and response is usually in the form of greater effort rather than abandonment of basic goals.

Inherent in Japanese social structure are additional values that have significantly circumscribed a wide range of pioneer behavior. With due regard to the evidence of change noted below, colonists continue to perceive themselves as members of a group of varying dimensions to which individual interests are subordinate. Group interests are sustained by feelings of obligation, and where individual and group interests conflict, the latter usually prevail. A premium is placed upon cooperative behavior, and most forms of cooperation are highly institutionalized. Discipline is considered essential to survival, and conduct prejudicial to group welfare is viewed with considerable resentment. Those who carry their share of the common burden are respected; those who avoid presumed obligations are subject to social strictures.

For immigrant colonists the threads of obligation have been somewhat frayed by changing meanings of "group." However, because the family is the matrix in which proper qualities of social conduct are supposedly crystallized, it is on the family that feelings of attachment are concentrated. The traditional Japanese family is rigidly structured, the hierarchy of authority firmly established, and individual members have well-defined roles that bind them to the family unit in a complex web of obligation and responsibility. Because these patterns are presumably projected to individual relationships with larger groups, the family is considered the cornerstone of the entire social structure.

In Paraguay, where pioneer behavior is not reinforced by unanimous social pressures, the defense of family solidarity is difficult. One approach has been to emphasize various aspects of the Japanese moral code. Sexual promiscuity is directly associated with weaknesses in Paraguayan family structure and is strongly condemned. Self-restraint in any context is valued, as are honesty, respect for elders, and decorum in the presence of others. Behavior contrary to moral precepts elicits social sanctions, but pressures upon individuals to conform are compounded by the fact that individual actions reflect upon the family.

Methods by which social conduct is kept within prescribed norms depend in large part upon appeal to the individual sense of obligation to community and family. Minor breaches of the social, legal, or moral order are met by group pressures, the effectiveness of which lies in the implied threat to survival that accompanies expulsion. Japanese are not accustomed to resolve conflicts on an individual basis, and differences are usually placed in the hands of community leaders. Personal injury is not characterized by the deep sense of loss of pride that can be regained only by personal vengeance, as it is among Paraguayans.

Serious breaches of order or acts of violence are the province of constituted authority in the form of representatives of the State, who judge and punish, presumably impartially, according to a long-established legal code. For colonists, this established authority retains some of the mystical overtones characteristic of prewar Japan in which individual participation was poorly developed and obedience and service were unquestioning.

Although the behavioral consequences of basic Japanese goals and values are directly related to specific choices made in creating the pioneer landscape, it is their role in acculturation that has determined the nature and extent of contributions made by Paraguayan culture. It is readily observable that immigrant and native goals, as well as acceptable methods of their pursuit, are widely divergent. Not unexpectedly, the magnitude of these differences has provided grounds for considerable conflict. Pioneers tend to view native society as decidedly primitive—an attitude that before 1946 was formalized in strictures against fraternization. Although few colonists would admit to such feelings today, substantial barriers to contact remain.[55]

Negative reactions to Paraguayan traditions focus upon social and moral factors, contamination from which is greatly feared as a source of social disintegration and hence a threat to ultimate successful achievement. However, colonists have difficulty isolating specific Paraguayan traits for dispassionate judgment, and these reactions inevitably extend to man - land relationships. Because colonists and natives pursue unrelated goals in productive behavior, Japanese are inclined to disregard Paraguayan solutions to environmental problems, and possession of a superior agricultural technology reinforces such attitudes. But acceptance of any obviously native trait is prejudiced by the view that to do so opens the door to disadvantageous if not disastrous compromises in fundamental values.

The basic elements of the Japanese value system noted above as introduced and sustained by immigrant pioneers are more or less ideal. On the behavioral level there is some departure from stated ideals, owing in part to expectable individual variations and the diverse social and geographic origins of the pioneer group. It is on the behavioral level, also, that changes are intruding to extend the range between precept and practice. In examining these changes, which are gradually altering the relation between introduced and native culture, it is important to distinguish between the reactions of the original immigrant generation and those of their Paraguayan-born offspring.

Among the original pioneers, who still constitute about 40 percent of the Japanese community, some ideal patterns have proved remarkably persistent. Until 1946 colonists were under little pressure to reorient cultural patterns. Some difficulty was encountered in attempting to reconstitute certain forms, particularly in cooperation. But the colonization company, in spite of evidence of mismanagement, stabilized the colony by providing a tangible link with Japan and a central authority connected to the home government. With the outbreak of World War II, colonists were further drawn together by nationalistic feelings, which were focused upon, among other things, being "good" Japanese.

By 1946, circumstances forced the Japanese to re-examine their cultural premises. By the end of the war the Paraguayan population outnumbered the Japanese, some of whom abandoned the colony as soon as wartime restrictions were lifted. Furthermore, since 1942 the colony has been administered by Paraguayan authorities. Thus the Japanese, in spite of their predominant economic role, are a distinct minority, forced to function within a social context they no longer control.

The defeat of Japan also produced significant repercussions in basic-value orientation. Japan's loss thoroughly demoralized colonists; ties with the home country were suddenly and completely severed, and pioneers, who already suffered from a sense of abandonment, realized they could expect nothing from a Japan prostrated by war and discredited by defeat. The implications of the war for cultural change among pioneers have yet to be examined fully. Some consequences have already been identified, but at least three interrelated reactions are germane to the present discussion.

a. Colonists despaired of returning to Japan, even for visits. As a consequence, behavior related to recognition of success, value, or status in Japanese terms began to lose ground as an imperative.

b. Removal of authority in the form of the quasi-governmental company administration deprived pioneers of a mechanism of social control. Without the company to plan and direct activities, colonists were no longer united in mutually agreeable purposes and were unable to completely counter the divisive forces operating within the group. The resultant deterioration of social cohesion has weakened group pressure as a means of circumscribing individual behavior.

Colonists also faced new instruments of control requiring considerable adjustment in traditional attitudes to authority. The Japanese were unprepared for the degree to which Paraguayans view authority as an instrument of personal aggrandizement through exploitation of others. Colonists still have not successfully bridged the gap between traditional moral precepts, obligation, and service, and the Paraguayan principle that involvement in politics and exploitation of influence are basic to self-defense. Superficially, pioneers retreat from participation in the political process,[56] avoid conflicts that might involve local authorities, and are resigned to the whims of those appointed to positions of control. On the behavioral level, however, there is evidence that the Japanese are gradually developing more realistic reactions to authority.

c. The pioneers' deep emotional involvement in the war, in association with the distinctive role of face in Japanese culture, has led immigrants to assume that defeat has largely discredited traditional ways. Colonists prefer to consider the past "closed" and to view the future in the light of current circumstances in which survival necessitates closer harmony with the Paraguayan milieu. The fact that pioneers consider their lives unalterably connected with Paraguay is in large measure responsible for the abdication of the older generation in favor of younger Japanese whose familiarity with native culture presumably makes them more malleable. It is worth noting that, although these attitudes serve to extend behavior beyond the traditional range between ideal and acceptable, many ideal patterns have not been surrendered but merely detached from their original cultural context. Thus morality, circumspection, hard work, and cooperation are valued because they are "good," not because they are Japanese.

Second-generation Japanese have been raised in a family atmosphere in which traditional values have usually been stressed, but the Japanese community no longer provides a precise mold into which their youth must fit. Because of internal disagreement, group pressures are dissipated in varying directions, and because Paraguayan culture offers an alternative, survival does not depend upon conformance. At the moment it is apparent that in spite of formidable pressures for assimilation, young Japanese are still strongly conditioned by values emphasized in the home. The relatively close-knit family environment counters the somewhat hostile atmosphere confronted in school or in the Paraguayan community, and compulsory military service or the fact that youth faces diminishing opportunities in the colony has not yet managed to cancel parental influence. Since Nisei have gained influence in the colony by abdication of elders (rather than through maturation within a specific system) and by proving capability in traditional terms, they are predictably disoriented with respect to their role in the colony. However, most Nisei prefer the relative security of the Japanese community and are willing to sacrifice a certain amount of individuality in order to continue functioning within it.

As long as the original pioneer generation is present in considerable numbers, younger members of the colony continue to perceive their survival in largely non-Paraguayan terms. Hard work, practical commercially oriented agriculture, family integrity, a sense of future, economic security, proper moral conduct, and, to some extent, institutionalized cooperation remain central motivations for behavior. However, Nisei, already faced with reduced and simplified forms of Japanese culture, find themselves increasingly separated from elders who do not perceive Paraguayan culture as they do and who have not experienced the same pressures for assimilation. The wedge between generations is in no way comparable to that found among immigrant populations in, say, the United States, but if Nisei are not particularly attracted to contrasting patterns of Paraguayan behavior, neither can they duplicate traditional conduct. Young Japanese, for example, do not share with their elders the concept of face and are not inhibited by tradition from realistic perception of the role of Paraguayan politics in everyday life. As the primary generation is removed by attrition, the guidelines for conduct, which are already fuzzy, will become even less distinct. At what point they will disappear cannot be determined without further study, but clearly the Nisei element is resigned to the eventual redefinition of the future in terms of survival in an essentially Paraguayan milieu.

CHAPTER 4

Summary
and Conclusions

THE case history of La Colmena suggests that the colony landscape, as the palpable product of a specific occupance system, holds some important keys to the nature of pioneering processes. The material evidence of environmental reorganization is particularly useful as a source of insights into changing cultural patterns within a geographic frame of reference. Reactions of postwar Japanese visitors to La Colmena, most of whom are astonished at the gulf separating them from Paraguayan pioneers, indicate that fundamental changes in behavior have indeed taken place. No doubt the degree of cultural divergence has been distorted by parallel changes in Japan as a result of the war and its aftermath. However, field investigations based upon comparison of current landscape elements with prewar Japanese norms confirm the existence of change, and although La Colmena settlers appear in some respects to be more resistant to change than other pioneer ethnic groups in Paraguay, the magnitude of the alteration in some aspects of behavior is significant.

In La Colmena, the complexity of form and function in the basic elements of the cultural landscape has been severely circumscribed. Of necessity, emphasis is placed upon provision of shelter and conversion of land into a productive medium through which other basic needs may be met. Thus, all Japanese have engaged in, and have concentrated most of their energies upon, construction of dwellings and the practice of agriculture. Because the settlement has in some respects failed to mature much beyond the pioneering phase, artifacts directly related to dwellings and agriculture continue to monopolize the rural landscape.

In sifting this landscape for evidence of change, basic functional components offer distinctive problems in interpretation. Structures, by virtue of their inherent characteristics, contribute insights into processes of change but are unsatisfactory as indexes for measurement. In La Colmena, exigencies of pioneering forced colonists to construct and occupy expedient structures, which could not embody the entire trait-complex associated with rural Japanese architecture; the resultant condensation was immediate, drastic, and, in most cases, permanent. However, as quasi-permanent landscape features, buildings are not subject to periodic adjustment in the light of acquired experience. Because few La Colmena pioneers have as yet faced the problem of replacing early expedient dwellings, most structures in the colony reflect the initial elimination of nonduplicable features but offer little or no indication of those subsequently acquired. Among colonists who have recently replaced original houses the surrender to Paraguayan tradition has been nearly complete, and the paucity of intermediate compromises suggests a considerable discrepancy between cultural change and the structural evidence.

By contrast, landscape elements associated with cultivation appear to offer more meaningful data to the study of the nature, causes, and consequences of alterations in pioneer culture. In La Colmena, successful farming remains the most practical and acceptable means of status achievement, and, as the fundamental basis of livelihood, agriculture has received a disproportionate share of attention. In addition, farming, although often greatly simplified in pioneering contexts, involves an enormous variety of problems and, therefore, is sensitive to a wider band in the spectrum of pressures applied to introduced cultures. Of significance also is the fact that Japanese pioneer agriculture, because of the focus upon annual crops, provides a concurrent view of cultural change as well as some hints of progressive developmental sequences from which origins and processes may be inferred.

Within the relatively short span of a quarter of a century, colony agriculture has evolved as a distinctive system of holding and exploiting land. In the trait-complex formulated around cultivation, elements traceable directly to Japanese rural sub-culture are preserved. However, most specific practices and attitudes contrast markedly with homeland traditions. Cultural changes inherent in this system reflect the pressures exerted upon original traditions by the impact of unfamiliar circumstances. The failure of the original fund of behavioral cues to provide solutions to new problems implies, though it does not necessarily require, some cultural readjustment. Presumably, the wider the gap between new problems and familiar frames of reference, the greater the potential for behavioral change; the more pressing such problems are in terms of survival, the more rapidly changes will occur.

In all phases of the pioneering process the Japanese have encountered problems outside the specific guidelines of basic traditions, and response in the form of behavioral compromise is expressed throughout the range of pioneer culture. Under the circumstances the abstraction of elements with geographic relevance is arbitrary. Even within the relatively restricted confines of the cultural landscape, the tracing of individual threads through the intricate web of interrelationships is not always possible. Nevertheless, an attempt is made here to isolate sources of pressure upon cues developed within the context of Japanese land and society and to associate these pressures with the elements of current land utilization to which they appear related. Included are circumstantial pressures developed from the basic demands and conditions of agricultural pioneering; economic pressures resulting from local patterns of production and exchange within which colonists had to rationalize their own productive behavior; event-sequence pressures evolving from the general march of historical events; environmental pressures derived from an unfamiliar physical fundament; and pressures for assimilation encountered through contact with native Paraguayans. The order of consideration is in no way intended as a measure of relative significance.

Circumstantial Pressures

The variety of conditions imposed upon pioneers by the simple acts of migration and agricultural colonization in a foreign milieu is impressive. All pioneer groups share the general inability to duplicate precisely original culture patterns, and the impoverishment in material culture, with concomitant shifts in attitudes, is usually immediate and drastic. In La Colmena, Japanese colonists, faced with opening and clearing new land, rapidly discovered that most accustomed tools and techniques were inappropriate, that traditional diet could not be followed, and that the press of time during the first three or four years excluded or severely compromised complicated concepts and practices.

The Japanese are unique among Paraguayan colonists in the degree to which prior planning influenced the basic attributes of the resultant settlement. Colonists, the settlement site, and the settlement form were carefully selected. The orientation and practical details of livelihood activities were objects of detailed planning, and a resident administration insured execution. Although many arbitrary decisions proved ill adapted to local circumstances, they established a basic complex of preconditions beyond control of the colonists themselves.

The process of emigrant selection, which in large measure determined the basic social structure of the pioneer community, had both direct and indirect repercussions in the evolution of colony land use. Preference for young pioneers assured a lengthy cultural continuity, and the emphasis upon family units, no matter how hastily constituted, circumvented labor problems and reduced both the incidence and range of pioneer - native contact.

In spite of presumably rigorous selection oriented toward suitability for agricultural pioneering, La Colmena settlers provided a cultural base that was far from homogeneous. To a certain extent pioneers, by their voluntary detachment from familiar contexts, select themselves. But the sharing of an agricultural colonization experience does not necessarily imply any common bond. In fact, among Japanese, motives for emigration were diverse, and both the degree of dissatisfaction with home culture and the desire to recreate accustomed patterns remain highly variable. In addition, La Colmena colonists came from a wide variety of regional, occupational, social, and religious backgrounds. The large number of industrial and white-collar workers included in the group shared varying amounts of basic rural subculture, and among farmers, differences in regional crop-ecological experience and former landownership and management patterns introduced other variables.

From such heterogeneous raw material the reconstruction of a Japanese agricultural village was out of the question, and there is no evidence that such was intended. The pioneer group, assembled from widely diverse elements, lacked traditional social relationships based upon kinship or reciprocal obligation, and in spite of increasingly close ties through later intermarriage, the intricate interweaving of activities remains absent from the social fabric. A few specific social organizations survive, but traditional aims and functions have been profoundly altered, and no such organization has proved particularly successful in preserving cultural identity, assuring conformity, or collectively managing various phases of colony life. The bases for cooperation, in particular, have been undermined.

Furthermore, the lack of uniform agricultural experience among pioneers facilitated manipulation of livelihood activities by colony planners and administrators, to whom pioneers were drawn by need as well as by the sense of discipline inherent in identification with Japanese national culture. By predetermining the basic orientation of economic organization, colony planners established the criteria for selection of the settlement site, the size and layout of individual parcels, and the mold that has shaped cultivation technology. Regardless of motives that may have prompted the Japanese government to seek and support emigration to Paraguay, La Colmena was apparently conceived as an essentially economic venture. Colonists were directed toward large-scale commercial agriculture in order to establish a viable and competitive economic unit as well as to assure both individual and collective security. The first clearings were planted to crops intended for sale, and subsequent plantings have also been structured largely according to practical economic considerations.

Within the rather narrow range of selections available, planners managed to acquire a site that met most of their essential requirements. Situational considerations excluded sites in established centers of pioneer settlement but mitigated

the problems of economic isolation. The emphasis upon forested
(i.e., cultivable) land was consistent with predetermined economic
aims. However, the area available for paddy cultivation proved
wholly inadequate for colony dietary needs. In addition, the
absence of natural pasture precluded the development of livestock industries and handicapped individual pioneers in the
keeping of animals as a source of energy or fertilizer.

In keeping with the economic orientation established by
planners, the settlement plan envisaged the placement of individual pioneer families on large rectangular plots. The resultant pattern of rural dispersion does not seem to have required
major adjustment; the urban nucleus that developed within the
colony has failed to attract farmers from their land. Undoubtedly,
however, isolation of individual family units has increased the
pressure upon social cohesion by eliminating the traditional
focus of contacts.

Although no pioneer has yet managed to clear all his land,
the area over which productive energies must be spread has
been intentionally extended beyond that normally cultivated by
prewar Japanese peasants. As a consequence, much traditional
Japanese farming technology proved immediately inappropriate
and was never introduced. Landscape evidence suggests that
some traditional patterns may be held as a general ideal; among
colonists with suitable land, some traditional paddy methods are
preserved. Apparently, also, in spite of the example of the
colonization company, most pioneers preferred to restrict initial
cultivation to relatively small portions of their total holdings.

However, as plantations have expanded, colony agriculture,
by pioneer admission, has grown carelessly exploitive and is
evidently becoming more so. To a significant degree the extension of cultivation and the concommitant drift toward a variant
of land rotation is associated with the economic pressures noted
below. But the effects of declining intensity with the diffusion
of effort over abnormally large acreages appeared early: Land
immediately adjacent to farmsteads, which was the first to be
cleared and cultivated, now lies fallow, denuded of topsoil,
depleted of essential nutrients, and underlain by indurated pans
as a result of continuous cropping coupled with scrupulously
clean tillage. In plots brought under cultivation in succeeding
years, colonists have seldom bothered to remove stumps or
other resistant forest debris, and plantations choked with
weeds are becoming increasingly common.

The continual growth in the scope of individual farming operations is closely associated also with the introduction of hired native labor and its increasing role in colony production. Unlike most other pioneer ethnic groups in Paraguay the Japanese have proved exceedingly reluctant to surrender personal participation in cultivation, and no pioneer farm is operated exclusively with hired labor. However, colonists have inevitably been drawn beyond the labor resources of their families, and Paraguayans are readily employed to supplement individual effort. The availability of cheap native labor has permitted the return to some traditional practices, notably the preparation and cultivation of paddies, but the over-all effect has been the reverse. Supplemental labor invites further extension of plantings, and Paraguayans are permitted to employ their own simple tools and techniques in the elemental tasks involved in opening and cultivating new land as well as in weeding older plots.

The crop complex was also predetermined. Specific selections, motivated primarily by economics, committed pioneers to a distinctive polycultural association of annual plants that has no counterpart in Japan, or, for that matter, in Paraguay. The most successful pioneer economies in Paraguay have been developed from perennial plantations of yerba, tung, grapes, coffee, and to a lesser extent citrus fruit. Japanese pioneers have experimented with these perennials, and perhaps 25 percent include one or more of them in their individual land-use patterns. However, their role is minor in La Colmena's economy.

The particular plants selected for emphasis have been drawn directly from the inventory of Paraguayan economic annuals. Although several plants have been adopted more recently by colonists themselves, the basic association differs little from that introduced by the colony administration in 1936. Cotton, with a long and relatively consistent record of profit in Paraguay, remains the principal source of farm income. However, pioneers have managed to capitalize upon the commercial possibilities inherent in almost all plants grown for sale or sustenance by native farmers. With the exception of mandioca, all crops currently grown are coincidentally within the range of traditional Japanese farming experience and do not seem to have offered any particular challenges to pioneer agricultural technology.

The essence of economic practicality evident in the specifics of land use extends to pioneer attitudes toward the land and its ownership. Colonists view farming less as a way of life to which they are committed by tradition than as a means to purely practical ends. As a result, the Japanese do not weigh their choice against the entire range of cultural preconception; elemental cost-analysis rather than custom or folkloric concepts guides the actual working of the land, and pragmatism rather than a sense of deep personal attachment binds the pioneer to his land.

In pioneer - land relationships not all traditional attitudes have been discarded. Land availability seems to have provided an important attraction to prospective colonists, and immigrants have consistently attempted to accumulate as much land as their individual resources permit, including acreage that cannot be immediately developed. Pioneers are thus distinguishable from prewar Japanese farmers not only by the amount of land acquired, but also by the development of surplus land as an essential quality of the landholding pattern. Land accumulation in excess of current cultivation needs has been motivated, at least in part, by Japanese concepts of family obligation, including the responsibility for branch families. It is entirely possible also that the association of land with status persists. However, the practice is consistent with the shift in pioneer agriculture from the traditional intensive cultivation of small units on a sustained yield basis toward a fallow-rotation system in which virgin forest reserve is a prerequisite.

Land accumulation, whether in response to social or economic necessity, has produced important side effects upon colony population. In the wake of numerous defections by Japanese colonists after the war, pioneers unwilling or unable to leave gradually acquired most of the abandoned lots. Paraguayans entering the colony purchased the remainder, and by 1956 all agricultural land within the colony had been pre-empted. Thus, although the Japanese population has actually declined slightly from the wartime peak, population pressures are already severe. Japanese find it increasingly difficult to provide land for branch families, and this form of traditional obligation is succumbing to pressure for space. Since pioneers also find it more and more difficult to accommodate colony youth within the settlement, the prospects for substantial growth of the Japanese element seem remote.

Economic Pressures

The involvement of Japanese pioneers in commercial agriculture has established them firmly within the framework of the Paraguayan economy. However, because of their choice of crops, La Colmena farmers are more acutely sensitive to local economic conditions than are pioneer groups engaged in specialized production of perennial crops, some of which have international markets. Unlike pioneers with essentially plantation economies, the Japanese have found themselves in direct competition with native producers. By virtue of superior productivity, larger operations, greater efficiency, and better organization, the Japanese have experienced little difficulty in acquiring a share of local markets, but they have been unable to escape the complex of economic constraints to which Paraguayan peasants are subject.

For Paraguayan farmers, locational factors, poorly developed transportation, and disorganized production, distribution, and processing are reflected in prejudicial price - cost ratios. Although low returns for agricultural produce affect primitive native production but little, they are generally insufficient to support more sophisticated cultivation methods. Japanese colonists have discovered that importation of machinery and even fertilizer is prohibitively expensive, and the ability of such tools to pay for themselves through increased yields has yet to be demonstrated.

This price - cost squeeze has done much to drive the Japanese toward their current land-use system. To attain accustomed standards, pioneers have felt it necessary to continually expand plantings in order to capitalize upon the fertility of virgin land as well as to enlarge plantations. Since retirement of land from production means loss of income, expansion is seldom accompanied by the requisite fallow of the native shifting cultivator. In fact, almost any conservation practice requiring the sacrifice of land, time, plants, or money is perceived as a luxury. The eventual establishment of double-cropping represents an additional response to economic necessity but has compounded land-use problems by hastening the deterioration of the productive base. The continuing necessity for opening new land is fundamental to the preservation of pioneering attributes in the land-use system.

In addition to pressing more land into production, intensifying effort by double-cropping, and hiring additional labor, colonists have attempted to increase profit margins through closer organization. Traditional cooperative enterprise has never fully developed, and enforced cooperation by the colony administration apparently compromised colony unity. In 1948, however, an agricultural cooperative was formed, and economic circumstances have since forced most pioneer farmers to join. It should be stressed that the cooperative is strictly economic with no direct relation to traditional Japanese forms. Its sole function is to promote the agricultural economy of its members, some of whom are native farmers.

Owing mainly to the small number of participants, the cooperative has made only modest headway in breaking the chain of circumstances that circumscribes individual economies. By mobilizing the productive energies of approximately 100 farmers, members have cemented their hold upon a share of the Paraguayan market. More importantly, combined resources have permitted purchase of a vehicle, opening and maintenance of road connections to markets, building of storage facilities, and construction of the means for processing agricultural raw materials. The cooperative performs advisory services and may channel farmers into other agricultural pursuits in the future, but its primary value at the moment lies in protecting farmers from the greatest barriers to profit: high freight-rates and speculator-middlemen.

In spite of expanded production and cooperative enterprise, La Colmena colony has not been outstandingly successful as an economic venture. Nevertheless, if Japanese accomplishments have not equaled those of German pioneers in central and southern Paraguay or those of Japanese immigrants to other parts of South America, La Colmena colonists have managed to far surpass native farmers. In so doing, they have created a productive nucleus to which many Paraguayans have been attracted not only as laborers but also as permanent settlers. As a consequence, the Japanese, although still economically dominant, now function within their own colony as a distinct minority.

Environmental Pressures

The physical attributes of the selected site presented colonists
with both prospects and problems. In the subjective sense, the
total environmental complex seems to have provided little
ground for conflict with traditional Japanese nature psychology.
La Colmena is generally assumed to possess a benign environment
with which individuals can readily "harmonize," and in some
places, resemblances to various parts of the home country are
fancied. Indeed, it is claimed that the presence of a substitute
Fuji functioned as a favorable omen in site selection and as a
sustaining influence in difficult times.

Notwithstanding pioneer preoccupation with local, hence
presumably well-adapted, crops, the agricultural environment
involved Japanese settlers in some vexing ecological problems,
and ultimate solutions contribute, in part, to the discrepancies
between colony agriculture and prewar Japanese farming. However, it is important to note that few specific practices can be
ascribed simply to faltering cues in the face of environmental
pressures. The gradual decline of clean tillage, for example,
may reflect recognition of the prejudicial effects of strong sun
and torrential rains upon bare soil. But because many pioneers
had little or no agricultural experience, the evolution of current
practices met little resistance from traditional preconceptions.
Furthermore, in most cases where some adjustment is actually
involved, a variety of factors appears to have intervened, and
the role of the environment is far from clear.

Colonists themselves tend to dismiss the influence of the environment. However, at least two elements—natural hazards and
lack of pronounced seasonal contrasts—are clearly involved in
the evolution of colony agriculture. Natural hazards may have
produced some specific responses: Malaria is often cited as a
cause of delay in paddy development, and incursions of locusts
are credited with a modest rebirth of community cooperative
spirit by focusing attention upon a common problem. Be that
as it may, locusts, hail, untimely frosts, and recurrent droughts
have resulted in several costly and discouraging crop failures
which, by retarding colony development, have further compounded economic pressures.

The effects of pronounced climatic variability and the lack

of seasonal regularity are exceedingly difficult to measure. Most colonists came from the less tropical parts of Japan and were accustomed to activities structured by the march of seasons and well defined by the festival of calendar and natural indicators, or both. Seasonal pressures greatly reduced the range of individual choice, and intensity of effort was subject to considerable cyclic variation.

In Paraguay, however, the absence of strict seasonal imperatives and natural keys to changing environmental conditions posed serious problems in the organization of an agricultural regimen. The establishment of gross ecological outlines for each crop proved to be a slow process often accompanied by failure, particularly of ill-adapted imported seed varieties. The necessity for prolonged experiment caused considerable delay in the establishment of the colony on a firm economic footing. Colonists eventually acquired sufficient experience to introduce double-cropping, but in prolonged planting, maturing, and harvesting periods there is considerable room for individual preference, and the specter of failure continues to militate against confidence in a single system. Regardless of timing in individual systems, energy output must remain constant throughout the year, and colonists remark, "Nature may customarily offer advantages, but it permits no rest."

Event - Sequence Pressures

The task of identifying all the events great and small during the last quarter of a century that have touched the lives of La Colmena colonists presents formidable challenges. For the myriad events obviously connected in some way with pioneer activity, the degree of relationship, the intensity of impact, and the nature and direction of response are difficult to assess accurately.

In terms of cultural processes, all other events are overshadowed by World War II. The direct involvement of Japan in the war firmly focused the homeland in pioneer consciousness. La Colmena seems to have escaped the disruptive effects of errant patriotism that plagued Japanese Brazilian colonies. If anything, Paraguayan pioneers were drawn more closely togeth

during the conflict. In general, however, the war, and particularly
its aftermath, served to weaken rather than reinforce national
and ethnic identity. The outbreak of hostilities immediately and
completely isolated Paraguayan colonists from contact with their
home country. Supplies of Japanese material goods, implements,
and furnishings were rapidly exhausted and could not be replaced.
By restricting the flow of immigration the war also arbitrarily
fixed the limits of the colony's Japanese population and its basic
social structure: Reinforcement of the original pioneer group
was out of the question, and colonists were prevented from con-
tracting for wives or sending for relatives. When the subsidy
and direction supplied by the colonization company were suddenly withdrawn, the 130-odd pioneer families rapidly discovered
that their combined resources were insufficient to sustain many
vital functions. In particular, the small size of the group militated against the establishment of schools, newspapers, social
organizations, or other mechanisms for the preservation of
cultural identity.

Paraguay's position in the war was curiously ambivalent, but
in 1943 La Colmena was "occupied" by civil and military authorities. No formal economic sanctions were imposed, but civil
liberties of the colonists were closely circumscribed. There is
ample evidence that enforcement of regulations was extremely
uneven, but colonists were technically forbidden to hold their
school classes, meet on any pretext, or travel beyond the limits
of the settlement.

The outcome of the war affected La Colmena settlers as much
as if not more than its outbreak or conduct. Paraguayan colonists were quick to accept the fact of the Allied victory, but reactions proved wholly consistent with traditional Japanese attitudes toward such matters. For the original pioneer group,
defeat placed considerable pressure upon many basic values;
colonists assumed that older notions, already stigmatized by
economic underachievement, were now thoroughly discredited
and that those responsible for imposing'them were no longer
eligible for colony leadership. On an individual and collective
basis, the decision was made to abandon former models and to
"look inward." Consequently the authority traditionally vested
in age and experience was consciously sacrificed to the younger
generation who, because they were free from rigid prejudices
and the stigma of failure, could presumably direct the colony

toward a system geared primarily to the local milieu. Older colonists have not been entirely successful in divorcing themselves
from responsibility for the colony's future, but traditional standards no longer automatically qualify as the principal test for
behavior.

Isolation of Japanese pioneers from their homeland lasted
much longer than the war itself. In 1953, a small group of La
Colmena settlers managed to call attention to their difficulties
and to reawaken Japanese interest in Paraguayan colonization.
Subsequently several small colonies of Japanese have been
established near Encarnación, and more are contemplated. This
revival of Japanese immigration has had surprisingly little
effect upon La Colmena. Colonists are sharply divided concerning their role in new ventures, but they make no attempt to con-
ceal their disappointment at the token financial assistance received
in 1958. Many of them are more than ever convinced that solutions to problems must come from within, and the search for a
closer adaptation to local realities continues.

Pressures for Assimilation

Of all the sources of pressures to which Japanese pioneers have
been exposed, those resulting from contact with the native
Paraguayan population are the most difficult to interpret. Even
with the focus restricted to essentially geographic phenomena,
evidence is highly subjective, and the record is easily misread.

The average rural Paraguayan is not particularly prepared
by his culture for the experience of foreign contact; he is not
outwardly hostile, but he is not renowned for tolerance of things
beyond the range of his own limited cultural horizon. Paraguayans
feel no compulsion to impose or even to impart native behavior;
thus, although Paraguayans frown upon Japanese fishing practices and consider colony agriculture irrationally destructive,
they have exerted little, if any, overt pressure to reorient pioneer
land-use or land-occupance patterns.

The employment of native labor has placed Paraguayans and
Japanese in close association. However, the relationship is
strictly economic, and the Japanese, as employers, are the dominant element. Where special skills are involved (tile-making,
carpentry), pioneers have often been forced to accept Paraguayan

forms along with native labor. In agriculture, such need seldom arises. Colonists have found it convenient under certain circumstances to permit native laborers to use their own tools and techniques. Paraguayans have occasionally contributed advice on everything from weeding methods to agriculture folklore, but the position of native workers precludes control over acceptance of counsel.

With the growth of La Colmena into an essentially Paraguayan community, the possibilities for pioneer - native contact have been greatly enlarged. In patterns of recreation and formalized social organization the two groups seldom intermingle, but in business and through the medium of schools, civil administration, and compulsory military service, frequent and regular association is unavoidable. Most of these contexts involve only the younger generation, and upon them devolve most of the resultant pressures. A Japanese school is maintained, but the bulk of formal education is acquired in an overwhelmingly Paraguayan environment, and the value of conformance is made abundantly clear. Here, also, young pioneers are exposed to the intimate interconnections between church, politics, power, and success. After formal schooling, Nisei youth are subject to two years of military service during which they are exposed to the lowest common denominator of Paraguayan society and are forcibly, if temporarily, pressed into the mold.

Whatever the over-all effects upon pioneer culture, there is little direct geographic evidence that this concerted assault upon Nisei value orientation has produced significant changes. In agriculture, the fundamental contrasts between native and pioneer goals persist, and land-use practices remain consistent with colonist aspirations. The durability of pioneer goals is indicated by the fact that they are promulgated by the colony's leading agronomist, now general manager of the cooperative; although born in Japan, he is Catholic, married to a Paraguayan, and a graduate of local schools, including the local technical agricultural college.

In agricultural pioneering, particularly during early phases, the struggle for survival exerts enormous pressures upon basic traditions. However, pioneer culture has not assumed its current character solely through the process of subtraction; the landscape of La Colmena is obviously more than a distillation of prewar Japanese culture in the face of hardship. Having indicated sources of pressures that laid foundations for change, it remains for me to identify the sources of ideas incorporated into current patterns.

Basic forms of pioneer occupance represent the integration of elements with a variety of origins, most of which have been altered to fit local exigencies. If the reservoir of Japanese traits appears more shallow than expected, the answer lies in omission rather than survival; the merits of individual land-use practices were prejudged, and colonists did not actively participate in many decisions affecting introductions. In the building of structures and the cultivation of rice, colonists appear to have attempted to reconstitute original patterns as nearly as individual circumstances and resources permitted. Within the framework of economic goals, which have changed very little, consistent elements of thrift, personal involvement in agriculture, and hard physical labor persist. A few specialized implements, particularly harvesting tools requiring specific manual dexterity, are also preserved. Some forms of social organization affecting land use were introduced but have gradually succumbed to pressures upon the entire social fabric; only vestigial forms with profoundly altered functions remain. However, in the initial structuring of the colony, a significant portion of Japanese rural tradition was consciously omitted and has not subsequently been introduced.

Planners responsible for deletion of many elements of Japanese culture also provided a complex of substitutes. The essential characteristics of agricultural orientation, organization, and conduct were molded from composite Japanese colonization experience elsewhere in South America, particularly in Brazil. The inapplicability of Brazilian ecological concepts caused considerable subsequent modification in practical details of cultivation on the basis of patient experiment. Examples were also sought in German colonies in central Paraguay, from which colonists acquired grapevines and tung seedlings as well as other useful plants and advice. In general, however, the Japanese accepted the basic outline provided by settlement planners, and experiments have been largely restricted to adapting preconceived elements to local conditions.

With the gradual breakdown of war-induced isolation in recent years, the range of possible examples for pioneers has been greatly expanded. Not only appropriate parts of Latin America but North America and Europe as well as Japan now function as sources of seed, implements, and technology. If colonists have been prevented by their depressed economy from capitalizing on many new ideas, at least their horizons are no longer restricted to the local milieu.

The imposition of the initial system and the extended range of available models have reduced both the incidence of invention and the impact of acculturation. Certainly at La Colmena the popular image of the resourceful pioneer must be qualified. Patterns of land occupance have evolved from cumulative experience within predetermined confines and amplified by later borrowings from other cultural contexts. The composite whole may be unique, but there is little landscape evidence to suggest invention of concepts, implements, or practices.

In the formation of pioneer culture, the contribution of native Paraguayan traditions is uneven. Structural types reflect a decreasing reluctance to accept native forms. Except for outbuildings, however, substantial urban rather than rural types provide the basic models. In agricultural land use Paraguayan influences are far less evident. The persistent divergence in goals has seriously prejudiced the value of Paraguayan advice or example. Paraguayans are freely accepted as units of energy, and the concomitant acceptance of some native patterns has been inevitable. Forms of labor relationships themselves are identical with Paraguayan practices. Pioneers prefer simple contractual associations, to which they were first exposed through the colonization company; however, the more common native form of resident laborers, involving prolonged peón - patrón relationships and responsibilities, has been gradually incorporated into the system. Colonists may have copied the practice from German pioneers, but it is more likely an outgrowth of contact with native laborers. Employment of Paraguayan laborers introduced simple native tools into the agricultural complex, but pioneer farmers themselves have adopted only the machete and the long-handled hoe. Beyond these elements, and the planting of mandioca (which may have come from Brazil), little else can be traced directly to borrowing from native culture.

The study of La Colmena is obviously incomplete. Facts have been selected and interpreted with an obvious bias. The risks of omission are unavoidable where the basic intent is the exploration of an approach rather than the exhaustive survey of a given areal unit. Within the mechanical, conceptual, and methodological limitations of the study, I am hopeful that sufficient evidence has been marshaled to validate the basic premise: The landscape provides a readable and reliable record of specific cultural elements and processes that invariably participate in the complex relationships between man and land.

Notes

CHAPTER 1

1 Paraguayan geology is summarized in Harrington (1956), and Eckel (1959). Geomorphology is interpreted in Carnier (1911), and Wilhelmy (1949).

2 Eckel (1959), p. 66, reports the alluvium to be "several hundred meters thick" near the Paraguay River.

3 Related structures appear on the west bank of the river in the vicinity of Villa Hayes and extend some 10 miles into the Chaco (ibid., Plate 1).

4 Thus isla and, particularly, costa are common elements of Paraguayan toponymy (e.g., Isla Margarita, Costa Ñu, Costa Verá, etc.).

5 Lack of pronounced seasonal changes in the level of the Paraguay River has been ascribed by many authors to flood of the river's upper course over the vast Gran Pantanal. The shallow "Lake Xarayes" thus created acts as a natural reservoir gradually releasing the surplus runoff downstream.

6 Schuster (1929), p. 73.

7 Barclay (Jan., 1909), p. 9. The author reports that in 1905, flood waters of the Alto Paraná dammed its major tributaries; the Iguazú rose 210 feet, causing the famous cataracts to disappear.

177

8 According to Barclay (ibid., p. 13), the Alto Paraná offers at least 14 feet of water for navigation at all times between Posadas and Guaíra, apparently owing to potholes worn in the basalt shelves by the main current.

9 "The Parguayans live in a natural paradise. They enjoy a mild climate, yet one which is not lacking in the stimulating effects of moderate weather change." James (1959), p. 283.

10 A notable exception was British Consul C. E. Henderson, whose weather data were published by Strachan (1885).

11 Mangels (1919), pp. 90-124. Mangels was German Consul in Asunción.

12 Moises Bertoni, a Swiss naturalist, came to Paraguay in the late 19th century and established several settlements along the Alto Paraná. His instrument data appear in many short-lived contemporary journals, most of which he founded and edited, e.g., Boletín de Meteorología Agrícola de la Estación Agrícola de Puerto Bertoni, Boletín Meteorológico de la Escuela de Agricultura, The Paraguay Monthly Review, Anales Científicos Paraguayos, etc.

13 Including Knock (1930).

14 Obtained from the files of Servicio Téchnico Interamericano de Cooperación Agrícola (STICA) with the kind permission of Mr. Lorenz of the U.S. Operations Mission to Paraguay, which became the U.S. Agency for International Development (AID) program to Paraguay in 1961. STICA was administered jointly by the United States and Paraguayan governments until early 1967 when total administration of STICA was transferred to the Government of Paraguay.

15 Wilhelmy (1950), pp. 130-133, quotes Bertoni's figure of 82 inches as the yearly average rainfall at Puerto Bertoni. However, observations in adjacent Misiones, as well as for Presidente Franco (Figure 9, p. 18), make this value seem far too high.

16 Ibid., p. 136. Wilhelmy's conclusions, based largely upon observations in adjacent Argentina, botanical evidence, and Bertoni's work, do not conform to the most recent meteorological data (see Figure 9).

17 See maps of isohyets in Schuster (1929), pp. 35-36. These maps have been widely copied and appear in more recent official and unofficial publications.

18 Wilhelmy (1950), p. 136.

19 Fariña Sanchez (Apr., 1946), p. 86, charts monthly rainfall from 1881 to 1944; records through 1950 are drawn from Clayton and Clayton (1959), pp. 1265-1271. Where sources overlap, they are not always in agreement.

20   Knock (1930), p. 210. No informants could be found who had wit-
      nessed snowfall in Paraguay.

21   Colonists along the Alto Paraná often quote this figure, the source
      of which I have not been able to determine. During the "calamitous"
      cold spell of 1917-1918, Bertoni (July, 1919) observed the following
      absolute minima: Puerto Bertoni, $26°$ F; Cambyretá (near
      Encarnación), $14°$ F; and Encarnación, $16.1°$ F.

22   MS weather records obtained from the library of the U.S. Weather
      Bureau, labeled "Ministro de Guerra y Marina, Dirección de
      Meteorología." My arrival in Paraguay coincided with a severe
      drought. No rain was recorded in the vicinity of the capital from
      January 15 to February 16. During this period, temperatures of
      above $109°$ F were recorded for nearly a week.

23   Mangels (1919), p. 96.

24   A severe frost in 1957 helped to bring financial disaster to Compañía
      Americano de Fomento Económico (CAFE), a new colonization -
      coffee-growing project near Pedro Juan Caballero.

25   For example, 1931 was an average year for Asunción, with 50 inches
      of rainfall. However, from June to September less than two inches
      fell. Fariña Sanchez (Apr., 1946), p. 86. Japanese colonists in La
      Colmena report crop failures from drought in 1941 and 1942, but
      the total rainfall for Asunción (80 miles to the northwest) for these
      years totaled 64 and 47.5 inches respectively.

26   Part of the town of Encarnación was leveled by a storm in the 1920's,
      but testimony and photographs of the damage are inconclusive evi-
      dence of whether or not a twister was involved.

27   Felix de Azara disclaimed botanical competence but made interesting
      observations on native flora (1943), pp. 41-45. The infamous abduc-
      tion and nine-year imprisonment of Aimé Bonpland by the Para-
      guayan dictator Francia gave the noted French naturalist little
      opportunity to botanize. The even less fortunate Swedish naturalist
      Eberhard Munck af Rosenschöld collected prodigiously for more
      than 20 years, but few of his specimens reached Europe, and in
      1869 he was executed by Francisco Solano López. See Paulin (1951),
      pp. 311-314. Augustin St. Hilaire used "Paraguay" in the title of
      various works, but his itinerary apparently did not include the region
      within the country's present boundaries. Other early workers and
      their contributions are reviewed in Schuster (1929), pp. 91-95.

28   Chodat and Hassler (1898-1907).

29   Including the excellent review of Paraguayan flora by Professor
      Hochreuther in Schuster (1929), pp. 91-119. Significant details have
      been added by Bertoni, whose most important general work was

"Resumen de geografía Botánica del Paraguay," (1907). Carl
Fiebrig was for many years director of the Botanical Garden in
Asunción. His most noteworthy general work was "La flora del
Jardín Botánico de la Trinidad-Asunción: Ensayo de un estudio
ecológico sobre la flora Paraguaya"; Vol. 1 (1921), Vol. 2 (1930).
See also Verdoorn (1945).

30   For the most recent and comprehensive such work see Michelowski
      (Dec., 1958), pp. 79-97.

31   Hamill (Jan., 1955), p.7.

32   The grove (not personally visited) lies approximately 30 miles from
      the river and consists of "several hundred trees" dominating an
      area of about 25 acres. The origin of this stand is disputed, but
      the prevailing view favors human agency, presumably that of Indians,
      who are known to have used the seed for food. See Michelowski
      (Dec., 1958), p. 80, and Hamill (Jan., 1955), p. 9. Concerning
      Guaraní consumption of Araucaria seeds, see Metraux (1948), p. 80.

33   Hamill (Jan., 1955), p. 7.

34   Langer (1935), p. 81.

35   Few authorities have offered to speculate on the origin of upland
      campo. Opinion favors natural presumably edaphic causes, but the
      matter awaits further research on Paraguayan soils and culture
      history.

36   Fiebrig (1930), p. 29.

37   Fiebrig and Rojas (1935).

38   Copernica Australies Becc., a near relative of the Brazilian
      carnaúba palm with which it is often confused. See Markley (Aug.,
      1953), pp. 309-311.

39   Markley (Jan. - Mar., 1956).

40   Bertoni (1907), pp. 167 ff.

41   Regarding the Indians of the Alto Paraná region, whom he studied
      in some detail, Bertoni (1918), p. 45, makes the following statement
      on campo burning (underlining mine):
          . . .sino que hoy día los indios también van tomando gusto en
      la graciosa diversión de incendiar los campos sin necesidad,
      bella cosa que han aprendido de los civilizados. . . .

42   Azara (1943), p. 42.

43   Azara (1943), p. 44, observed "forests" of uncultivated bitter oranges
      and concluded that they resulted from Spanish introductions. How-
      ever, owing to the close integration of the tree with native flora

and the fact that it appears far removed from the sites of any known settlement, some authors have concluded that the orange is native to the region. One such writer bolstered his argument with the fact that a "wild" bittersweet variety has a Guaraní name (apepú). See Bourgade la Dardye (1892), pp. 222 ff.

44 Legend ascribed the introduction of Bermuda grass to the English railroad company who did so for the purpose of securing roadbed banks. Johnson grass was apparently brought to Paraguay from Argentina by Bertoni for experiment but escaped into surrounding agricultural land. Langer (1935), pp. 97-98.

45 Tirado Sulsona et al. (1954). A note on field methods, p. 4, emphasizes the preliminary reconnaissance nature of the survey:

> The report is based on observations made at intervals of 100 kilometers, whenever it was possible. In some instances aerial observations were made in order to coordinate specific areas as a whole. Profile observations were made whenever a change in external soil characteristics and vegetative associations was apparent.

46 Informant: Sr. Emilio Gloss, son of the colony's founder, now 80 years old, living in Encarnación and functioning as honorary Brazilian Consul. Malaria also struck the Japanese settlement of La Colmena in its early stages, seriously depleting the labor force and thus retarding colony development.

47 According to Bertoni (1918), p. 30, Sinulium, spp.

48 Sarcopsylla penetrens (ibid., p. 32).

CHAPTER 2

1 Regional inventories along more traditional lines are available. The most thorough compendium is Schuster (1929). More recent and somewhat capsulized works include Pendle (1954); Sermet (Jan. - Mar., 1950); and Raine (1956).

2 Paraguay (1955).

3 The total enumerated was 1,328,452. To this total 30,000 Indians have been added and 50,000 "for whom no information could be obtained" to yield the official estimate of 1,408,000 (ibid., p. 20).

4 Municipalidades are not defined, but the standard table divided them into categories based upon population, including "less than 200" to "more than 100,000" (ibid., pp. 22-23).

5   Several local censuses conducted in conjunction with other investiga-
    tions concur. See, for example, Reh (1946), p. 14.

6   Service and Service (1954).

7   Azara (1904), pp. 426–427 and 442, notes that in 1785 there were
    approximately 10,000 Negroes and mulattoes in Paraguay, about
    60% of whom were slaves. In 1744 the town of Emboscada, north-
    east of the capital, was settled entirely with Negroes and mulattoes
    as a buffer against Indian raids (ibid., pp. 47–50).

8   Cadogan (Mar., 1951). In addition, some 20,000 Indians are thought
    to occupy the Paraguayan Chaco.

9   Reh (1946), p. 8.

10 Paraguay (1955), p. 21, enumerates 649,114 men and 679,338 women.
    Discussion of the historical aspects of this problem is well beyond the
    scope of the present work. However, superficial examination of the
    documentary record suggests that the effects of the War of the
    Triple Alliance upon the Paraguayan population may have been
    greatly exaggerated.

11 Service (1954).

12 Service and Service (1954), p. 31.

13 Ibid., p. 33.

14 Ibid., p. 283. The primacy of the Services in this field has apparently
    resulted in a more or less uncritical acceptance of their conclusions
    in this country. See particularly Julian Steward's introduction to
    their volume on Tobatí. In Latin America, however, their work was
    received with mixed reactions. For a particularly critical review
    by an authority on Guaraní mythology, see Cadogan (June, 1956).
    With the Services' over-all conclusions I find it difficult to disagree,
    except perhaps for the astounding comparison in agricultural produc-
    tivity of Paraguayan campo with the prairies of Iowa (ibid., p. 54)!
    However, on the basis of limited personal fieldwork, it seems to
    me that the door to several issues has been prematurely closed.
    I do not contend that the record has been misread—only that the
    sample was insufficient to settle many questions definitively and
    that much more work is needed before the specifics of Paraguayan
    behavior can be assigned an origin or unraveled in terms of the
    complex processes of their evolution. For further discussion of
    this matter see Stewart (1963), pp. 184–187.

15 The persistence and prevalence of Guaraní, largely detached from
    its original cultural context, is unique in Latin America. In Service's
    view the language is less an aboriginal survival than a cornerstone
    of modern national consciousness. Certainly Paraguayans are

inordinately proud of Guaraní and associate it intimately with their concept of ethnic-national identification. But this may be a rather late phenomenon and can also be viewed as an effect rather than a basic cause of the continued predominance of the language. The concubinage of harems of Indian women by the relatively few Spaniards, and the rapid emergence of mixed offspring, for whom communication in the mother's tongue was most natural, seem fundamental to the process. Furthermore, because of the direct involvement of Spaniards in Guaraní kinship, little status contrast, and restricted outside contacts, Guaraní, carrying no stigma, was far more useful in everyday problems such as courtship and labor relations than Spanish, which was reserved for more remote affairs of state. Service is disinclined to credit the Jesuits with much influence in the formation of Paraguayan culture, but their refusal to teach Spanish in the missions, their isolation of a part of the Indian element from Spanish contact, and their efforts to convert Guaraní to a written language may have contributed in some measure to the survival of the aboriginal tongue while other cultural elements were being diluted.

16 See Julian Steward's introduction to Service and Service (1954), p. xiv. In the preface following, the authors state that their work was made extremely difficult because even in Tobatí, in the central region, "they [the peasants] lived in the more remote areas and often spoke little Spanish or none at all. . . ." (ibid., p. xxiii).

17 Paraguay (1955), p. 25. The linguistic data are broken down in the following manner:

Language	No. of Inhabitants
Guaraní only	481,039
Spanish only	56,887
Spanish and Guaraní	645,034
Other	16,411

18 According to informants, the itinerant peddler—usually of foreign extraction—was important in rural exchange. However, there seem to be few such peddlers today.

19 Mid-19th-century travelers to Paraguay reported that the ramada doubled as a sleeping platform to enable the sleeper to escape insects, but this practice is no longer in evidence.

20 Paraguay (1955), Table 33, p. 34.

21 The census was conducted from 1942 to 1944, and the results were published in 1948 as the Censo de Agricultura del Paraguay, 1942-43, 1943-44 (1948). Another census was taken in 1956, but only preliminary results were available at the time of this study. Based on fieldwork, it appears that information collected in the early 1940's

continues to reflect the approximate condition of Paraguayan agriculture.

22   Ibid., Table 1, p. 16. Chacra is defined as any agricultural unit with at least one hectare under cultivation. As a result, many essentially nonfarming estates were included, and an indeterminate number of peasant farms with less than the requisite area planted were unfortunately excluded.

23   Ibid., Table 2, p. 50.

24   Paraguay (1951). San Lorenzo is 7 miles east of Asunción.

25   Lesser (1944), pp. i, ii.

26   Paraguay (1948), Table 11, p. 72. For present purposes 7 hectares (about 17 acres) is considered the dividing line between peasant farms and other forms of agricultural land utilization.

27   Lesser (1944), p. 1. More recent information was acquired by interviews with the President and other officials of the Instituto de Reforma Agraria and with technicians in STICA.

28   Paraguay (1948), Table 12, pp. 75-76. Although Table 11 lists 59,702 farms operated by ocupantes, 70,247 farmers work all or part of their land in that capacity.

29   Service and Service (1954), p. 51.

30   Azara (1943), p. 199.

31   Paraguay (1954), pp. 11-46.

32   Few farmers will admit to lack of interest in landownership, and there is a small but often volatile literature on the plight of the landless Paraguayan. See particularly the very useful Lucha por tierra en el Paraguay, Pastore (1949). However, the evidence indicates that in spite of the usual political, economic, and social rationalizations evoked to explain the dispossessed peasant, landownership is not high in the Paraguayan value system.

33   The high ranking of citrus fruit, bananas, and mangoes stems from the common practice of planting several varieties of fruit trees around dwellings. Commercial plantings occupying large fields are thus not so common as figures indicate.

34   The native palm Acracomia totai (cocotero) produces an edible nut with some dietary and market value. Although some of these coconuts may be consciously planted, they more commonly invade cultivated plots as volunteers and are not to be considered as part of the domesticated agricultural plant complex.

35   Habillas, according to the Services (1954), p. 60, refers to beans of the "navy" variety.

36   Production of yerba, wheat, and probably grapes is largely in the hands of foreign colonists, hence these plants are not so prevalent in Paraguayan peasant agriculture as the figures indicate.

37   Service and Service (1954), pp. 67-71.

38   Azara (1943), pp. 59-66, notes what apparently was a type of primitive pod corn, but no such variety was personally observed.

39   The Services, apparently following the agricultural census, call these "cowpeas," but exactly what species is involved I have been unable to determine. Service and Service (1954), pp. 71-73.

40   According to the Services (1954), p. 71, labor is massed to harvest beans to prevent rotting from exposure to rains.

41   Ibid., p. 75.

42   The Services' implication that the "coconut" is included among the cultivated fruits is misleading. Service and Service (1954), pp. 73-74. It may be that the seeds are occasionally planted, but the extraordinary speed with which the palm pioneers new clearings makes planting almost unnecessary.

43   Paraguay (1948), Table 14, pp. 80-82.

44   Some informants report that a second, narrower blade (yvyrá pepé) is used for actual planting, in which case the resemblance to the Spanish arado cuchillo would be even more precise. The morphology of Spanish plows has been examined in considerable detail by Caro Baroja (1949). See especially Figure 68 on page 58, which is reproduced from Townsend (1791).

45   These implements and their introduction into the Spanish Colonies are noted in Foster (1960), pp. 55-56. A photograph of a rastra de púa (a primitive wooden spike rake) appears in Barrios (1956), p. 13. However, no such instrument was personally observed.

46   Paraguay (1948), Table 14, pp. 80-82. Other competing forms of cart have been introduced by foreign colonists. Several lighter horse-drawn four-wheeled vehicles (carro polaco, carro menonita) have become popular outside their original colonies.

47   Service and Service (1954), p. 63, note that the digging stick is uncommon, and in the central zone this seems to be so. However, informants disagreed, some insisting that it was best for planting tobacco, onions, alfafa, and rice. Planting with a digging stick was personally observed near San Pedro and also near Horqueta. Digging sticks were also observed on two occasions among Mbyá-Guaraní Indians.

48   The list is intended as nothing more than a sample. Service and Service (1954), pp. 250-252, describe other beliefs connected with

natural phenomena, and I have avoided repetition. It is probable that
both lists only scratch the surface of the subject.

49   This word does not seem to have an English or Spanish equivalent
     but was summed up by informants thus: People who possess teterasú
     are lazy, out-of-sorts, or otherwise of mala virtud. They refuse to
     get out of bed or to take part in family labor or social activities.
     Such persons contaminate others by touching or looking and are
     responsible for a wide variety of other mischief, including the
     drying up of wells and crop failure. The concept is apparently a
     variant of the evil eye.

50   Azara (1943), p. 199. "En efecto solo cultivan la tierra los que no
     puèden proporicionarse tierras y ganados para ser estancieros o
     no encuentran otro modo de vivir. En esta caso de ser agricultores,
     está mas de la mitad de los españoles del Paraguay."

51   Reh (1946), p. 81.

52   Paraguay (1948), pp. 194–195 and 200–201.

53   Other barnyard fowl are not numerous, but guinea fowl are occasion-
     ally kept, and the Services noted ducks of an unspecified variety.
     Service and Service (1954), p. 80.

54   Cows milked for home consumption are of no special breed, but
     simply small, poorly conformed criollo range cattle that have been
     acquired for the purpose. The common process for cheese-making
     with the cuajo (dried calf stomach) is described by Reh (1946), p. 81.
     According to the Agricultural Census, about two million kilos of
     cheese were produced in 1942 - 1943, or about 5 pounds per individual.
     Paraguay (1948), p. 210.

55   Statistics on farm income included in the Agricultural Census are
     illuminating in this regard. Of 94,390 farms reporting, only 497
     completed the agricultural year 1942 - 1943 without some income,
     although for most small therefore presumably peasant-operated
     farms, the annual income was extremely modest. For example, on
     chacras between 7.5 and 10.5 acres the annual income was about
     $100. The role of bartering and neighborly sharing is impossible
     to calculate, but it is likely that the total economic potential of the
     average peasant is at least double his calculable cash income.

56   Paraguay (1948), pp. 132 and 156.

57   Ibid., pp. 112-114.

58   The mixto is an integral part of Paraguayan commerce. The term
     is applied to conveyances fitted out to carry passengers but having
     the primary function of carrying cargo. Trucks visit most of the
     small towns in the central region on a scheduled run to collect

produce. Passengers are accepted but take second place to cargo and are refused when there is no more room.

59 Feelings toward some of these, such as the attitude of authorities, or avarice on the part of revendedores, are to some extent justified, but malevolent spirits, an inexorable Creator, or plain bad luck are freely included.

60 Paraguay has long hoped for the discovery of oil in the Chaco. However, the Union Oil Company terminated operations in 1949, and the Pure Oil Company followed suit in 1960, and although the possibility of future discoveries cannot be ruled out, the prospect is not likely. Concerning other mineral resources see Eckel (1959), p. 95.

61 Paraguay's forest utilization and resources are discussed in Klein (1946).

62 In at least one instance a study was conducted regarding the feasibility of linking forestry directly with colonization. See Hamill (Jan., 1955).

63 In 1946, pastoral industries accounted for 33% of total exports, but by 1957 the figure had dropped to 12.4%. U.S. Department of Commerce (1954), pp. 86-87, and Ortiz (Mar., 1958), p. 1. The latter figure should undoubtedly be adjusted upward considering the apparently sizable contraband trade with Brazil. The over-all decline in trade of cattle and cattle products has many causes, not the least of which is the entrance of the Paraguayan government into the meat business.

64 The German colonists of San Bernadino survived and eventually prospered by turning to dairying. The Australian utopian settlement of Nueva Australia postponed disaster for several years by raising cattle.

65 In 1958 two new road projects were begun: (1) the Trans-Chaco road, from Villa Hayes, on the Paraguay River to eastern Bolivia, and (2) a road connecting Asunción to the Brazilian port of Paranaguá via a bridge over the Alto Paraná River near its junction with the Iguazú. The ultimate significance to Paraguay of these new international connections is debatable, but they represent at least a theoretical possibility of escape from Argentine control of Paraná River traffic.

66 The total railroad mileage for Paraguay is 660. However, more than half is privately owned narrow-gage line employed largely in logging, and more than 285 of Paraguay's total track miles are located in the Chaco. Paraguay (Jan. - Mar., 1957), p. 44.

67 See also Lindman (Mar., 1952).

68 Yerba maté was first planted by the Jesuits in their Paraná missions, but cultivation ended with their expulsion in 1767. Bonpland's experiments with yerba cultivation in Misiones ended with his abduction and the destruction of his entire establishment. Failure of Parguayans themselves to develop yerba plantings is usually rationalized by folkloric conceptions of the mysteries of the plant's reproductive processes (e.g., "the seed must pass through the stomach of a bird") and insistence that the wild product is far superior to cultivated varieties. However, a colonist in Nueva Germania named Neumann is credited with revolutionizing patterns of production by the discovery that planting yerba is technically fairly simple.

69 <u>Macho</u> is defined by the Services (1954), p. 233, as ". . . a concept which lumps sexual desire and potency with aggressiveness, bravery, pride, and physical vigor into one single characteristic." <u>Vivo</u> is a bit more elusive. It includes behavior that is contrary to the social and legal order but the term is not attached to the ordinary malcontent or petty criminal. A <u>vivo</u> lives by his wits and takes every opportunity to defy convention. If, as often happens, his acts lead him into brushes with the law, his reputation is enhanced, provided that his deeds are accomplished with a show of bravado and disregard for the risks involved. Such a person is not to be trusted but is often secretly admired.

CHAPTER 3

1 For a history of immigration and pioneer settlement in Paraguay, see Stewart (1963), pp. 196-238.

2 Normano and Gerbi (1943), pp. 21-23.

3 Compañía Nipo-Paraguayo de Colonización, Sociedad Rural Limitada (SRL), which was founded by former residents of La Colmena, later underwritten financially by the Japanese government, and eventually integrated into a federal union of immigration associations (Nippon Kaigai Kyokai Rengokai). Information obtained from Antonio Kasamatsu, one of the company's founders.

4 Compañía Pro-Fomento de Migración Japonesa, S.A., founded as a speculative venture by Japanese financial interests, with participation of the Japanese government on the basis of funds borrowed from the United States. Information obtained from Dr. Aiji Nishio, Director, Asunción Branch of Pro-Fomento.

5 Data from MS records of Sr. Kasamatsu of Cía. Nipo-Paraguayo. Official Paraguayan statistics compiled from various official sources

list Japanese immigration through 1956 as follows:

1936	no data	1943	0	1950	0
1937	149	1944	0	1951	1
1938	99	1945	no data	1952	0
1939	113	1946	no data	1953	0
1940	48	1947	no data	1954	18
1941	111	1948	0	1955	766
1942	0	1949	0	1956	238
	520		0		1,023

TOTAL 1,543

Statistics obtained from the Japanese Embassy in Asunción indicate a total of 4,390 immigrants to Paraguay between 1899 and 1958: from 1899 to 1941, 521; from 1955 to Dec., 1958 (postwar period), 3,869.

6   Decreto No. 1026, 30 de abril, 1936. Reproduced in Paraguay (1939), p. 82.

7   A company similar in organization and function to the present quasi-governmental entity (note 4). However, "to facilitate relations with the Paraguayan government," a private company emerged (Paraguay Taku-shoku) headed by one Kunito Miasaka, who is considered the founding father of the colony and is presently president of the Banco Japonesa do Brasil, São Paulo, Brazil. Information was obtained from informants, particularly Sr. Kasamatsu, who was an agronomist on the original survey team.

8   In 1939, an adjacent tract of 5,700 acres known as Mbocayaty was added to the colony.

9   For the same period (1938 through 1945) the average annual precipitation for Asunción was 51.6 inches.

10 For reasons noted later, many colonists refer to a prominent, roughly conical peak of the Cerro Apitaguá as Fuji-san. There is little likelihood that "Fuji" will become established as a formal place-name.

11 In normal usage, quinta refers to suburban villas associated with a considerable amount of land. Those in La Colmena are small agricultural properties ranging between 5 and 50 acres.

12 Fujii and Smith (1959), p. 9.

13 Usui (1958), pp. 147-148. There are 9 families noted as entering after the war, bringing the total to 147 families consisting of 897 persons.

14 Ibid., pp. 279-284. Colonists entering La Colemena came from 36 prefectures. However, of the 93 families and 27 branch families encountered by Usui in 1956, more than one third came from prefectures in Hokaido and northern Honshu.

15   According to Usui, the "main" natural disasters were: 1936, drought;
     1937, hail, locusts; 1938, flood; 1944, drought; 1945, frost; 1946,
     locusts; 1947, frost; 1952, locusts; 1954, frost (ibid., pp. 155-156).

16   The administration represented the Paraguay Colonial Bureau, a
     semiofficial agency charged with managing and promoting Japanese
     settlement in Paraguay (ibid., p. 130).

17   Thompson (revised 1947), p. 41.

18   All attempts to acquire 1950 census data for minor civil divisions
     proved unsuccessful. The figure cited represents the consensus of
     estimates by leading citizens of La Colmena.

19   Although 9 families entered the colony after the war, a total of 94
     families have left La Colmena, most going either to Argentina or
     to Brazil. Usui (1958), pp. 288-292. Of these, 54 were presumably
     composed of the original settlers, the remainder consisting of branch
     families established in the colony. Colonists rationalized these
     defections as a necessary weeding process; many even insisted that
     such defections were beneficial. A typical comment: "If everyone
     stayed, soon there would be no room to buy land for our sons." It
     is clear, however, that abandonment left a residue of resentment
     among those who remained. Not only was the number of laborers
     necessary for cooperative enterprise dangerously reduced; those
     who left were also accused of "mining" their land to accumulate
     enough capital for passage, thereby ruining a sizable portion of the
     colony.

20   The shift has also been made without particular difficulty in the
     settlement of northern Japan.

21   Embree (1939), p. 93. Embree notes that in the village studied (on
     the island of Kyushu) priests advised that dwellings should face
     south.

22   Serious outbreaks of malarial fever plagued the colony in its forma-
     tive years, and it is possible that the attempt to escape mosquitoes
     by elevation of the sleeping quarters is a response to this problem.

23   Japanese architectural styles are reviewed in many places. Among
     the principal sources for the present chapter are Ogawa et al. (1956);
     and Kitao (1956). Both works are in Japanese.

24   Yet both separate kitchens and outdoor ovens are used in rural
     Japan, apparently because of the fear of fire. See Embree (1939),
     pp. 90-94.

25   The owner, Namio Mitue, was 14 years old when brought from Japan.
     At the age of 26 he assumed family leadership and management of
     the farm and has been remarkably successful. Unfortunately, photo-

graphs of his house were among a number that failed to develop acceptably.

26 Information obtained from Sr. A. Tomita, surveyor and head of the colony land office.

27 In 1956, 27 of the 120 families present in the colony were listed as branch families. Usui (1958), pp. 279 ff.

28 Fujio Moriya, untitled, unpublished MS submitted to the faculty of the Institute of Agronomy (San Lorenzo) for the degree of "Agronomist" (1948). This short but useful work is an essay on the agricultural progress of the colony by one of its younger members, currently general manager of the agricultural cooperative.

29 Recent data on agriculture obtained from the files of Cooperativa La Colmena, SRL.

30 The colony's only "rancher," who had had no agricultural experience before coming to South America, is head of one of the families from Brazil. (See also note 40.) In 1940 he bought one cow and slowly accumulated a herd as a future investment. To support the enterprise he was forced to buy large blocks of campo along the colony's northwest border. Currently he has about 100 head and is the principal source of meat for the town market. Since he also owns several quintas, which are intensively farmed, he still considers ranching as a profitable sideline.

31 Usui (1958), p. 129.

32 The average family size for all colonists entering between 1936 and 1941 is 5.9. The close relation between large families and successful colonists has been noted by many students of pioneer settlement and is certainly evident in Paraguay. Japanese planners currently supervising new settlement enterprises feel that pioneer families should consist of six members.

33 Labor was recruited on the basis of the kumi (see pp. 143 ff). Whether or not colonists received compensation for working on "public" projects is not clear.

34 The changing role of German agricultural pioneers in Paraguay is discussed in Wilhelmy (1949), pp. 70 ff.

35 Adoption for various purposes, including enlarging family labor supply, has been common in Japan. The keeping of genin, although a pattern that began to disappear with the shift toward tenant farming in the 18th century, is a case in point. See Smith (1959), pp. 14 ff, 184 ff.

36 The nata, a short, heavy, chisel-shaped knife, performs similar functions for woodsmen and mountain farmers in Japan. The nata

is a common tool in newer Japanese pioneer settlements near Encarnación but is not used in La Colmena. The Brazilian brush-hook, which is found among Brazilian-German colonists near Encarnación, was brought to La Colmena by families from Brazil, but only two families now use it.

37 Informants report a similar tool in common usage in Japan, although it is constructed and employed somewhat differently. The seeder found in La Colmena was apparently borrowed from the Pflanzen-maschine used by German colonists near Villarrica.

38 The tan is one tenth of a cho and hence roughly one tenth of a hectare.

39 Part of the reason for hiring additional labor for various tasks is the extraordinary amounts of time these tasks consume. It is estimated, for example, that clearing a hectare of forest requires 35 man-days. Plowing a 20-acre lot with oxen requires 30 days, with one day added for every day of rain.

40 The most notable exception to the abandonment of fertilization and other intensive farming techniques is Kichigoro Moriya. As one of the settlers originally from Brazil, but without previous agricultural experience, Moriya was responsible for early planning, including some of the mistakes that seriously jeopardized the future of the colony. He has since more than redeemed himself by conducting and publishing research on Paraguayan farming problems and by preserving much traditional agricultural technology in the operation of his singularly model plantation. He is the colony's only "rancher" (see note 30) and has so integrated cattle breeding and farming that he is able to collect several tons of manure annually for application to 15 cultivated acres. He has actually experimented with rotation systems; he seeds leguminous cover crops between rows of plants, and every scrap of vegetable waste is conserved for future incorporation into the soil. Moriya has also experimented with more than 200 plants, including tea, coffee, yerba maté, cinnamon, cinchona, and a wide variety of fruits. His farm, totaling 25 acres in crops and orchards, has not declined perceptibly in productivity in more than 20 years of continuous cultivation. In spite of the fact that these practices are thus kept alive in the colony, Moriya's example is not emulated, and his advice is seldom sought, perhaps because of loss of face resulting from earlier failures.

41 Former farmers point out that a similar body of folk beliefs was once prevalent among the farming population in Japan, and although occasionally still encountered in isolated rural areas, lore has largely disappeared with increasing demands upon farmers and the recent spread of modern agricultural technology. Typical comments, referring to prewar Japan: "In Japan there is no time to wait for the

proper phase of the moon." "The old people sometimes talked of these things, but the young no longer listen."

42   The provision of farm credit is undertaken by the wealthier colony farmers and merchants on a cash-interest basis. It is doubtful that traditional forms of mutual financial aid, such as the ko, have been preserved. For a description of ko in Kyushu, see Embree (1939), pp. 139 ff.

43   In Paraguay, the state of the agricultural economy of a colony is reflected accurately in the number of boliches or other small mercantile operations established by colonists as a substitute or supplement for farm income.

44   Chipa is a rough bread made from maize meal or mandioca flour; sopa paraguaya, often referred to by Paraguayans as their national dish, consists of maize bread to which cheese and other ingredients have been added; locro is maize prepared in a form similar to hominy. A comprehensive survey of Paraguayan foods and recipes is to be found in Service and Service (1954), pp. 306 ff.

45   For example, foods, like agricultural plants, possess "temperature," i.e., all foods are either "hot" or "cold," and these qualities condition when, how, and with what they are eaten (ibid., p. 260).

46   During the Independence - Founder's Day fiesta in 1958 the Japanese youth organizations erected a booth for the sale of osushi and beer in order to raise funds for various projects. Almost any foreign visitor eventually will be offered a "Japanese" meal, but by observation and the frank admission of the host, it is seen that many essential ingredients are lacking.

47   A visitor to the colony 18 months after its founding noted: "Wherever we went we were received with hospitality. Kettles boiled to brew the maté, that soon had taken the place of tea and was almost without cost." Thompson (revised 1947), p. 43.

48   The only festival currently celebrated is the combined holiday commemorating Paraguayan Independence Day (May 14) and Colony Founder's Day (May 15). Festivities, which may last a week or more, include the population of the entire district. The Japanese hold sporting events, operate a booth at the carnival-fair, and offer a show of skits and songs, but the celebration is overwhelmingly dominated by the Paraguayan community.

49   Several informants note that funerals are occasionally still conducted "in the Buddhist way," but evidence is contradictory. In the public cemetary, which serves the entire settlement, there are numerous Japanese-style grave markers, but few are recent, and there is no evidence of cleaning, offerings, or other attention to

burial sites. No birth observances are preserved. Marriages are celebrated by Paraguayan civil ceremony. However, receptions, when held, often continue to include simple Japanese gift exchange and food patterns.

50   Although evidence is contradictory, it is doubtful that Paraguayan landowners were invited to join the kumi. Certainly none have done so.

51   Several examples of kumi from Kyushu are thoroughly examined by Embree (1939), pp. 112 ff.

52   Of the families entering La Colmena after the war, only two remained in 1958, and in 1960 one of these moved to Argentina. Thus, the role of new colonists in reviving cultural ties is negligible.

53   Since colonists can now view their experience with considerable hindsight, it is difficult, on the basis of their testimony alone, to reconstruct certain highly significant factors. However, evidence gained from literature and contacts with the Japanese community in California (some of whom came from South America) suggests that in spite of careful selection, many emigrants had no intention of remaining abroad. The return of prosperous colonists to Japan—particularly those settling in the United States—stimulated others to follow who viewed their emigration as a temporary stay during which wealth could be accumulated rapidly, thereby enhancing status of self and family upon return. No colonist in La Colmena admitted such feelings, but the ultimate departure of half of the original settlers in search of greater opportunity is indicative, and there is reason to believe that many of those remaining were prevented from moving only by their economic circumstances.

54   Unlike Brazilian Germans, who incorporated the horse into pioneer status patterns, La Colmena settlers have found little coincidence in Japanese and Paraguayan status symbols and show no interest in local prestige indicators. See Willems (Apr. - June, 1944).

55   It is worth noting that such barriers are not necessarily one-sided. Prior to 1946, Paraguayans were somewhat awed by Japanese technical skill, their extraordinary capacity for hard labor, and the rapid and profound changes these produced in La Colmena's landscape. Japan's role in World War II drew additional respect, because Paraguayans are inordinately proud of their own military achievements and greatly admire qualities associated with combat. With the defeat of Japan the aura of superiority began to evaporate, and increased familiarity produced marked changes in Paraguayan attitudes. The divergence in goals, and perhaps racial considerations, have evolved as sources of abrasion. Paraguayans continue to express grudging admiration for Japanese labor, but work is not high among

native values, and colonists are generally regarded as hopelessly out of phase with the primary ingredients of native culture.

56   In Paraguay, voting is mandatory for all citizens over the age of 18. However, to my knowledge, no immigrant colonist has been naturalized, and many of the Nisei are still too young to vote.

References

Azara, Felix de, Geografía física y esférica de las provincias del Paraguay y Misiones Guaraníes, Talleres de A. Barreiro y Ramos, Montevideo (1904), 478 pp.

Azara, Felix de, Descripción e historia del Paraguay y del Río de la Plata, Editorial Bajel, Buenos Aires (1943), 383 pp.

Barclay, W. S., "The River Paraná: An Economic Survey," Geogr. J., 33 (1), 1-40 (Jan., 1909).

Barrios, Vicente, Zona de Coronel Oviedo, Servicio Téchnico Interamericano de Cooperación Agricola (STICA), Bol. 207, Asunción (Aug., 1956), 18 pp.

Bertoni, Moises, "Resumen de geografía botánica del Paraguay," An. Cient. Paraguayos (Puerto Bertoni), Ser. I (2), II Parte, 126-190 (1907).

Bertoni, Moises, "Condiciones generales de la vida orgánica," Descripción física y económica del Paraguay (Puerto Bertoni), 12 (1), 48 (1918).

Bertoni, Moises, "La temperatura mínima secular de 1918," An. Cient. Paraguayos (Puerto Bertoni), Ser. II (5), 354-355 (July, 1919).

Bourgade la Dardye, Emmanuel de, Paraguay: The Land and the People, Natural Wealth and Commercial Capabilities, Geo. Philip & Son, London (1892), 243 pp.

Cadogan, Leon, "Breves consideraciones sobre algunos aspectos del folklore paraguayo." [Review of Service, Tobatí], Rev. Antropol. (São Paulo), 4 (1), 63-66 (June, 1956).

Cadogan, Leon, "El problema de la población Mbyá-Guaraní del Departamento de Guairá," Bol. Indig. [Inst. Ind. Inter-Americano] (Mexico), XI (1), 74-91 (Mar., 1951).

Carnier, Karl, "Paraguay: Versuch zu einer morphologischen Betrachtung seiner Landschaftsformen," Geogr. Ges. Jena, Mitt., 29, 1-50 (1911).

Caro Baroja, Julio, "Los arados españoles—sus tipos y reparticiones," Rev. Dialectología Tradiciones Populares (Madrid), 5, 36-96 (1949).

Chodat, Robert, and Emil Hassler, Plantae Hasslerianae, Impr. Romet, Geneva (1898-1907), 2 vols.

Clayton, H. H., and Francis Clayton, eds., World Weather Records, Vol. 1, MC 79, Before 1921 (1927); Vol. 2, MC 90, Publ. 3218, 1921-1930 (Reprinted 1944); Vol. 3, MC 105, Publ. 3803, 1931-1940 (1947); Smithson. Inst. Misc. Collect., Washington, D.C. [See also U.S. Department of Commerce, World Weather Records (1959).]

Concurrencia del Banco Agrícola del Paraguay a la Exposición Internacional de Agricultura de Buenos Aires, en el Centenario de la Revolución de Mayo, 2nd ed., H. Kraus, Asunción (1911), 256 pp.

Eckel, Edwin, Geology and Mineral Resources of Paraguay—A Reconnaissance, U.S. Geol. Surv. Profess. Pap. 327, Washington, D.C. (1959), 110 pp.

Embree, John F., Suye mura, a Japanese Village, Univ. of Chicago Press, Chicago (1939), 354 pp.

Fariña Sanchez, Teófilo, Investigación estadística de las precipitaciones pluviométricas en Asunción del Paraguay," Rev. Meteorol. (Montevideo), 5 (18), 78-88 (Apr., 1946).

Fiebrig, Carl, "La flora del Jardın Botánico de la Trinidad-Asunción—Ensayo de un estudio ecológico sobre la flora Paraguaya," Rev. Jard. (Asunción), 1, 13-63 (1921); 2, 9-75 (1930).

Fiebrig, Carl, and Teodoro Rojas, "Flora y gea de la parte nordeste del Paraguay—Resultados de una expedición realizada por el Jardín Botánico en 1933/34," Rev. Jard. Bot. (Asunción), 4, 51-81 (1935).

Foster, George M., Culture and Conquest; America's Spanish Heritage, Viking Fund Publ. Anthropol., No. 27, Chicago (1960), 272 pp.

Fujii, Yukio, and T. Lynn Smith, The Acculturation of the Japanese Immigrants in Brazil, Latin Amer. Monogr. Ser. 8, Univ. of Florida Press, Gainesville (1959), 56 pp.

Grahame, Stewart, Where Socialism Failed, John Murray, London (1912), 266 pp.

Hamill, E. B., Pulping Possibilities of the Alto Paraná Forest (Preliminary Study of Possibilities of Integrated Forest Industries to Aid in the Development of Colonization of the Paraguayan Alto Paraná), STICA, Asunción (Jan., 1955), 41 mimeo. pp.

Harrington, Horacio J., "Paraguay," in W. F. Jenks, ed., Handbook of South American Geology, Geol. Soc. Amer. Mem. 65 (1956), pp. 99-114.

James, Preston E., Latin America, 3rd ed., Odyssey Press, New York (1959), 942 pp.

Kitao, Harumichi, ed., Graphic Architecture (in Japanese), Vol. 20, Roof: Vol. 33, Fence and Wall; Vols. 37 and 54, Farmhouse, Shokukusha, Tokyo (1956).

Klein, Morton A., A Forest Survey of Paraguay, STICA, Asunción (1946), 106 pp.

Klein, Morton A., The Forest Resources of Paraguay; A Special Report, Inst. Interamer. Aff., Washington, D.C. (1946).

Knock, Karl, "Klimakunde von Südamerika," in Koppen and Geiger, eds., Handbuch der Klimatologie, Vol. 2, Part G, Gebruder Borntaeger, Berlin (1930), 349 pp.

Langer, Alejandro, "Ensayo de cultivo de plantas forrajeras para ganado vacuno de la Sección Agrícola Experimental del Jardín Botánico (1925-28)," Rev. Jard. Bot. (Asunción), IV, 81-114 (1935).

Lesser, Alexander, Land Ownership and Land Tenure in Paraguay, Coord. Interamer. Aff., Res. Div., Washington, D.C. (1944), 42 pp.

Lindman, Bertram H., The Transportation Problem of Paraguay, Inst. Interamer. Aff., Washington, D.C. (Mar., 1952), 98 pp.

Mangels, H., Paraguay: Wirtschaftliche, naturgeschichtliche und klimatologische Abhandlungen, F. P. Datterer, Munich (1919), 255 pp.

Markley, Klare S., "Caranday—a Source of Palm Wax," Econ. Bot., 9 (1), 39-52 (1955). [Revision of "Caranday—a Source of Palm Wax," J. Amer. Oil Chem. Soc., 30 (8), 309-311 (Aug., 1953).]

Markley, Klare S., "Mbocayá or Paraguay Cocopalm—an Important Source of Oil," Econ. Bot., 10 (1), 3-32 (Jan.-Mar., 1956).

Metraux, Alfred, "The Guaraní," in Julian H. Steward, ed., Handbook of South American Indians, Smithson. Inst., BAE Bull. 143, Vol. 3, Washington, D.C. (1948), pp. 69-94.

Michelowski, Michael, Breve curso de geobotánica para los alumnos de la facultad de Agronomía y Veterinaría, STICA, Asunción (Dec., 1958), 109 mimeo. pp.

Moriya, Fujio, Untitled thesis on the agricultural development of La Colmena, submitted for the degree of Agrónomo, facultad de Agronomía y Veterinaría, San Ramon (1948), 15 typescript leaves.

Munck af Rosenschöld, Eberhard, Algunas cartas del naturalista sueco don Eberhard Munck af Rosenschöld escritas durante su estadía en el Paraguay, 1843-1869 (transl. from Swedish by Ernesto Dethorey), Biblioteca e Instituto de Estudios Ibero-Americanos de la Escuela de Ciéncias Económicas, Stockholm (1955), 29 mimeo. pp.

Normano, J. F., and Antonello Gerbi, The Japanese in South America; an Introductory Survey with Special Reference to Peru, John Day, New York (1943), 135 pp.

Ogawa, Toru, Taro Wakamori, and Soiichi Yoshida, eds., Japanese Local History of Culture (in Japanese), Vol. 7, Kyushu, Kawada Shobo, Tokyo (1956).

Ortiz, Maximo V. A., Manual estadístico del Paraguay, 1951/1957, STICA, Bol. 218, Asunción (Mar., 1958).

Paraguay, Departamento de Inmigración, Leyes de tierras y decretos reglamentarios, Anexo, Ley de Inmigración, Asunción (1924), 72 pp.

Paraguay, Departamento de Tierras y Colonias, Compilación de leyes y decretos ordenada por Carlos Pastore, Presidente del Departamento y Ejecutada por Carlos A. Rolón, Asunción (1939), 325 pp.

Paraguay. Ministro de Agricultura y Ganadería, Censo de Agricultura del Paraguay 1942-43; 1943-44, Bureau of the Census, Washington, D.C. (1948). [Prepared by STICA.]

Paraguay. Ministro de Agricultura y Ganadería, Problemas de la tierra en la compañía reducto, San Lorenzo del Campo Grande (resumen), Sección Económica, STICA, Asunción (1951), unpublished MS, 11 numbered leaves.

Paraguay, Instituto de Reforma Agraria, Compilación de leyes y disposiciones reglamentarias relativas al régimen de la tierra en el Paraguay, Asunción (1954), 320 pp.

Paraguay, Ministro de Hacienda, Dirección General de Estadística y Censos, Anuario estadístico de la República del Paraguay, 1948-1953, Asunción (1955), 120 pp.

Paraguay, Ministro de Agricultura y Granadería, Resultados preliminares del Censo Agropecuario, 1956, Asunción (1958), 30 pp.

Paraguay, Ministro de Hacienda, Dirección General de Estadística y Censos, Bol. estadístico Paraguay (Asunción), trimestral, ano 1 (1), (Jan.-Mar., 1957, to the present).

Pastore, Carlos, La lucha por la tierra en el Paraguay: Proceso histórico y legislativo (Antequera), Montevideo (1949), 191 pp.

Paulin, Axel, Svenska öden i Sydamerika, P. A. Norstedt, Stockholm (1951), 618 pp.

Pendle, George, "Eliza Lynch and the English in Paraguay, 1853-1875," History Today, (May, 1954), pp. 346-353.

Pendle, George, Paraguay, A Riverside Nation, Roy. Inst. Int. Aff., London (1954), 115 pp. [2nd ed., 1956.]

Raine, Philip, Paraguay, Scarecrow Press, New Brunswick, N.J. (1956), 443 pp.

Reh, Emma, Paraguayan Rural Life: The Survey of Food Problems, 1943-45, Inst. Interamer. Aff., Washington, D.C. (1946), 130 pp.

Rengger, J. R., and M. Longchamp, Historischer Versuch über die Revolution von Paraguay und die Diktatorial-Regierung von Dr. Francia, J. G. Gotta'scher Buchhandlung, Stuttgart and Tübingen (1827), 163 pp.

Rojas, Teodoro, "Paraguay," in Franz Verdoorn, ed., Plants and Plant Science in Latin America, Chronica Botanica, Waltham, Mass. (1945), pp. 121-125.

Schuster, Adolph N., Paraguay: Land, Volk, Geschichte, Wirtschaftsleben und Kolonisation, Strecker & Schroeder, Stuttgart (1929), 667 pp.

Sermet, Jean, "Le Paraguay," Les Cahiers d'Outre-mer (3rd year),
    9, 28-65 (Jan.-Mar., 1950).
Service, Elman R., Spanish Guaraní Relationships in Early Colonial
    Paraguay, Anthropol. Pap. Museum Anthropol., No. 9, Univ. of Michigan
    Press, Ann Arbor (1954), 106 pp.
Service, Elman R., and Helen S. Service, Tobatí: Paraguayan Town,
    Univ. of Chicago Press, Chicago (1954), 337 pp.
Smith, Thomas C., The Agrarian Origins of Modern Japan, Stanford Univ.
    Press, Stanford, Calif. (1959), 250 pp.
Stewart, Norman R., "Recent Trends in Paraguayan Immigration and
    Pioneer Settlement," Geogr. Rev., LI (3), 431-433 (1961).
Stewart, Norman R., Japanese Colonization in Eastern Paraguay: A Study
    in the Cultural Geography of Pioneer Agricultural Settlement, un-
    published Doctoral dissertation, Dept. Geogr., Univ. of California,
    Los Angeles (1963), 452 pp.
Strachan, R., "Results of Meteorological Observations Made at Asunción
    (1855-57)," Quart. J. Roy. Meteorol. Soc., II, 238-241 (1885).
Thompson, R. W., Voice From the Wilderness [publ. also as Germans
    and Japs in South America], Faber and Faber, London (1941), 360 pp.
    [Revised 1947.]
Tirado Sulsona, Pedro, Joseph B. Hammond, and José R. Ramirez,
    Clasificación preliminar de los suelos y tierras del Paraguay, STICA,
    Asunción (1954), 165 pp.
Townsend, Joseph, A Journey Through Spain in the Years 1786 and 1787,
    C. Dilly, London (1791), 3 vols.
U.S. Department of Commerce, Bureau of Foreign Commerce, Office of
    Business Economics, Investment in Paraguay. Conditions and Outlook
    for U.S. Investors, U.S. Govt. Printing Office, Washington, D.C. (1954),
    110 pp.
U.S. Department of Commerce, Weather Bureau, World Weather Records,
    1941-1950, Vol. 4, U.S. Govt. Printing Office, Washington, D.C. (1959).
U.S. Department of Commerce, Weather Bureau, Manuscript Records,
    Paraguay (microfilm), Washington, D.C.
Usui, Shigeru, Twenty Year History of La Colmena, the First Japanese
    Colony in Paraguay (in Japanese), Tokyo (1958), 295 pp.
Verdoorn, Franz, ed., Plants and Plant Science in Latin America,
    Chronica Botanica, Waltham, Mass. (1945), pp. 121-125.
Warren, Harris G., Paraguay—an Informal History, Univ. of Oklahoma
    Press, Norman (1949), 393 pp.
Wilhelmy, Herbert, "Aufbau und Landformen des Alto-Paraná Gebiete,"
    Petermanns Geogr. Mitt. (Gotha), 92 (1), 32-38 (1948).
Wilhelmy, Herbert, Siedlung im Südamerikanischen Urwald, Krogers
    Verlaganstalt, G.m.b.H., Hamburg-Blankenese (1949), 104 pp.
Wilhelmy, Herbert, "Zur Klimatologie und Bioklimatologie des Alto-
    paranagebiets in Südamerika," Petermanns Geogr. Mitt. (Gotha),
    94, 130-139 (1950).

Willems, Emilio, "Acculturation and the Horse Complex Among German-
Brazilians," Amer. Anthropol., 46 (1), 153-167 (Apr.-June, 1944).
Willems, Emilio, and Herbert Baldus, "Cultural Changes Among Japa-
nese Immigrants in Brazil, in the Riberia Valley of São Paulo,"
Sociol. Social Res., 26 (6), 525-537 (July-Aug., 1942).